GW00374777

A parents' guide to helping children (5-11 years) to solve mathematical problems

Professor Valsa Koshy

Sally Paggetti

Gwyneth Try

Elizabeth Koshy

Published by:
enrichchildrenslives

First published 2020

Designed by Gwyneth Try, Horsedrawn Desktop Publishing
Cover design by Rebecca Try

ISBN-13: 978-1-900905-26-8

ISBN-10: 1-900905-26-4

All rights reserved. No part of this publication may be reproduced or transmitted in any form or by any means, electronic or mechanical, including photocopy, recording, or any information storage and retrieval system, without permission in writing from the publisher.

Table of Contents

About the Authors

Professor Valsa Koshy

Prior to joining Brunel University, Professor Valsa Koshy was a primary classroom teacher and a member of the mathematics advisory team of the Inner London Education Authority. During her 25 years of academic career at Brunel University she has led Professional Development courses on the teaching of Mathematics for hundreds of primary school teachers. She has taught trainee teachers and carried out a significant number of research and development projects relating to mathematics education, many of which were funded by the UK Government Department for Education. Working with parents to help them to support their children's learning has been a significant part of her work. **Valsa** obtained a PhD in Mathematics Education from Exeter University UK. She was recently awarded an MBE for her services to Education in a variety of roles over four decades.

Sally Paggetti has taught mathematics at Secondary School level for 25 years, the last 15 of those as an Advanced Skills Teacher, specialising in developing teaching strategies and programmes for enriching children's mathematical learning. For the last 12 years she has worked as a maths consultant at Brunel University working on a range projects, including the latest project funded by the Mayor of London and the UK Department if Education on using talk to enrich children's learning and raising their achievement. (www.TalkMathsTalk).

Gwyneth Try has many years of experience as a Teacher Assistant working with teachers and with children offering them support. This experience has provided her with many valuable opportunities to explore parents' perceptions of mathematics, as well as identifying what their needs are to support their children's learning. Gwyneth has worked with Valsa Koshy on several mathematics projects aimed at enriching children's thinking and learning. Her special talent is in making activities accessible and practical for the users. She has both produced and designed a medley of enjoyable activities for teachers to work with children.

Dr Elizabeth Koshy has worked as a General Practitioner and as a medical researcher at Imperial College, London. She has a passion for supporting parents on all aspects of wellbeing and she believes that developing good habits in the learning of mathematics, such as determination, persistence and hard work can give children a sense of contentment and contributes to their general happiness. She has worked with many children and has found that being engaged in mathematical problem solving can enhance children's wellbeing by building up their resilience and, that it helps them to overcome their fear of failure and become more optimistic.

Acknowledgements

Our aim in writing this book is to provide parents with practical strategies for teaching children to become effective problem solvers. We have drawn on two main sources for selecting the content of this book: our experience of working with teachers for several years, and, working with individual children and groups with a range of abilities on all aspects of mathematical learning. Although it is impossible to name all the people who have influenced our thinking over the past few years, we would like to express our gratitude to all of them. We would especially like to thank the following people:

♦ All the teachers and children we have worked with and from whom we have learnt a great deal. They have kept us aware of an important principle in providing support for both parents and teachers: *the need to provide practical and manageable guidance and suggestions within a framework which facilitates logical thinking, reasoning and reflection.*

We dedicate this book to our own children. Watching their development of mathematical and problem solving skills has contributed to our own learning process, which has guided us in writing this book.

Chapter 1

Introduction

What is problem solving?

We encounter problems of different kinds in our everyday lives. Problems that we have to solve can range from simple ones, such as finding mislaid keys, to more complex ones like sorting out money and budgets, or finding suitable and satisfying employment. In all these cases, a solution needs to be worked out.

A simple definition of a problem is:

A situation which requires a satisfactory solution.

In problem solving, we undertake an unknown journey towards reaching a successful solution. The good thing is that we can all get better at problem solving by careful thinking and systematic working. It also helps to talk about the problems with others and sharing ideas, if and when it is possible. A problem that is solved nearly always makes us feel happier and that feeling is rewarding. It also stimulates our brain.

Helpful points to become good problem solvers

There are some useful points for you to remember when solving problems.

- Do not rush for a solution. Take a little time to think. Ask: "what is the problem?" And "what is a satisfactory solution?"

- Remember, there are nearly always many different ways to solve a problem and generate different outcomes. As we get used to analysing the problem, thinking about it and systematically following suitable steps, we become more efficient.

- After a problem has been solved, it is always useful to evaluate the way we have arrived at the solution. Ask: "are there any other ways in which the problem could have been solved?". This kind of reflection helps us to become more effective in problem solving.

Problem solving in mathematics

Problem solving in mathematics is similar to other problem solving activities, but in order to solve mathematical problems you need to know and use facts, skills and procedures which are part of learning mathematics. You also need to develop a specific set of strategies for problem solving. We describe them as developing mathematical processes.

What are these special skills needed for problem solving in mathematics?

The five specific objectives of learning mathematics put forward by Her Majesty's Inspectorate in the UK (HMI, 1985) provide us with a very helpful framework when considering what the effective teaching of mathematics involves. These five objectives, which continue to be used in most mathematics education literature, are:

- Facts

- Skills

- Conceptual structures

- General strategies

- Personal qualities

A brief discussion of what these objectives are and how they are special in the learning of mathematics and in problem solving are now discussed. These are examined in more detail by Koshy (2017) in her book *'Teaching Number With Understanding'*.

Facts

Children need to learn and remember correct facts. They need to learn mathematical terms such as number names, names of shapes and names of operations. They need to recognise and use mathematical signs such as +, −, x, = and so on. Mathematical notation, such as decimal points and percentages (%), needs to be recognised and understood. Remembering facts such as 5 + 5 = 10 or 6 x 7 = 42 is useful for two reasons. First, such facts when committed to memory make it possible for children to use them fluently and with speed and, secondly from 'known facts', it is possible to derive new facts; for example, if you know 5 + 5 = 10, then 5 + 6 can be worked out with reasonable ease. Learning facts, therefore, empowers children. We need to encourage this. Other facts that children need to remember relate to measurement, money and angles. For example, knowing facts such as 1 Kilometre = 1000 metres, 1 Metre = 100 centimetres and 1 centimetre = 10 millimetres is necessary to solve word problems.

Skills

An important landmark in mathematics education in the UK was the publication of the Cockcroft Report (1982) which describes skills as an integral part of learning mathematics and explains that:

> *Skills include not only the use of number facts and the standard computational procedures of arithmetic and algebra, but also of any well established procedures which it is possible to carry out by the use of a routine. They need not only to be understood and embedded in the conceptual structure but also to be brought up to the level of immediate recall or fluency of performance by regular practice.*

Skills include number operations and routine procedures. These messages which are reinforced in many documents since, including the most recent National Curriculum in England, (DfE, 2013) are useful and should be taught and practised. Children often practise skills without understanding the rationale behind learnt procedures. Learning mathematical skills without understanding the ideas behind them does not lead to effective problem solving.

Conceptual Structures

The Cockcroft Report (1982) describes conceptual structures as 'richly interconnecting bodies of knowledge'. HMI (1985) puts forward a powerful argument in favour of aiming for a sound conceptual understanding.

> *No concept stands alone: for example, subtraction is linked with addition, multiplication is linked with addition and division, and percentages are linked with fractions and decimals. In fact, each concept is linked with many other aspects of mathematics... Indeed, being 'good at mathematics' is dependent on the ability to recognise relationships between one concept and another.*

Talking about mathematical ideas such as properties of number, using appropriate practical apparatus and discussions of procedures and misconceptions are some of the strategies which will help children to build robust conceptual structures. A deep understanding of mathematical ideas is vital in becoming a competent problem solver.

General Strategies

These are related to strategies we use for solving problems and carrying out investigations. When children are involved in problem solving, they will need to draw on three aspects of mathematical learning: knowledge of facts, appropriate skills and procedures, and problem solving processes. Mathematical problem solving processes are discussed in more detail in Chapter 2.

Personal Qualities

Attitudes are important in all learning. Enjoyment and pleasure are, undoubtedly, contributing factors to all aspects of learning, and solving mathematics problems is no exception. We all know about the fear, panic, anxiety and the feeling of inadequacy about learning mathematics felt by many pupils and adults during their school days and beyond. As positive attitudes can lead to success and more confidence, this is an aspect which needs careful consideration.

Think about ... time for flash back

Some of you may remember your mathematics lessons in school. Many of you could manage the different skills such as addition, subtraction, multiplication and division and learning multiplications tables by memorising them. These elements of learning have been required of all children. What may be missing is providing children with a range of experiences using the knowledge.

Parents have told us that they used to feel anxious when they had to work out word problems which involved systematic thinking and persevering. This anxiety has not changed much over the past years but it is now steadily changing. Children in most countries, including the UK, are encouraged to solve problems which involve careful thinking, use of logic and systematic working. Based on what parents and children have told us, here is a set of advice you should find useful.

The golden rules

- Remember and tell the children that mathematical problem solving – working out word problems, playing mathematical games and solving puzzles are very enjoyable activities and do give you much pleasure and enjoyment. These activities can be undertaken together – parents and children – so, consider them as 'treats'; they can provide tremendous satisfaction when completed.

- Don't tell children that you 'hated' maths or didn't like solving problems. Children's attitude to learning mathematics has been changing over the past few years. Most schools are moving away from encouraging children to learn mathematical rules and ideas by 'rote' and without understanding.

- Mathematical games provide great opportunities for problem solving. Board games, such as 'Snakes and Ladders' and other track games which use dice, will help children to enjoy mathematics. In order to help children with problem solving you will need to ask them the right questions while playing the games. There are many examples of effective questioning in Chapter 3 of this book.

- Develop fluency in your children's learning of facts, such as $13 + 9 = 22$; double $48 = 96$. Mental arithmetic and knowing multiplication tables do save time, when children are solving problems.

- There are many opportunities to solve problems in everyday life – at home, whilst shopping, travelling or doing a topic or a project. Again, asking the right questions is really important. There are a number of practical ideas provided in Chapter 3 of this book.

- All children can get better at problem solving if they are given encouragement and opportunities. It is a myth that problem solving only benefits very able children.

- Praise children for their effort. But remember that over praising can lead to complacency and giving up if confronted with challenging work which takes time and more effort.

- Talk about effective strategies for problem solving (see Chapter 2). These have been proven to help children to become effective problem solvers.

- Research has shown that our intelligence is not fixed and that the right kind of stimulation can help children to make more connections in the brain and become more effective and successful in all learning. Problem solving provides ideal opportunities for such stimulation.

- Talk to children while they are solving problems. Ask them to tell you what they are doing. Explaining ideas helps them to understand ideas, grow in confidence and revise strategies.

- Record steps in solving problems. It helps to keep track of directions taken and spot mistakes.

- It is important that children feel it is OK to make mistakes. It shows they are being challenged and will be able to tackle more demanding work as a result of re-thinking strategies.

- Problem solving can take time. Working systematically is more important than speed. With encouragement and discussion of strategies, children will acquire both speed and confidence.

Possible difficulties with problem solving

What are the possible difficulties experienced by adults – teachers and parents – in training children to be effective problem solvers?

- Quite often children do not understand where to start when solving a problem. Practice makes it easier and it is important to remember that the time spent on problem solving is worthwhile, as it benefits children in many ways as learners of mathematics.

- Children are sometimes put off by word problems which may appear daunting. It is also possible that children with reading difficulties lose their confidence and give up. Reading the problem together can help.

- Children may sometimes worry about taking too long to solve a problem. The message then should be that it is not speed that matters and, with experience everyone can become better and faster problem solvers. Quite often children will get faster with tackling problems.

What are the benefits of problem solving?

- First, it is a very enjoyable and rewarding activity. It may take some time before children start enjoying the processes involved, but once they are used to it they get excited and find the experience fulfilling.

- Problem solving activities help children to use and apply mathematics in a variety of situations. This is the main purpose of its inclusion in the mathematics curriculum.

- It helps children to make connections between mathematical ideas which lead to a deeper understanding of mathematics and its associated rules.

- Problem solving is a creative and exciting activity. Therefore, it can help children to develop positive attitudes to mathematics.

How solving mathematical problems can boost children's mental wellbeing

How the mind works can affect our lives. Creative thinking and the use of imagination help children to develop problem solving skills, which can transfer to life skills. When trying to solve a mathematical problem, it is not always obvious how to start. Children wonder and ask: what mathematical words and processes are required? Their response to this question, when it leads to a satisfactory solution to the problem, gives contentment and so contributes to their general happiness.

Determination is an important ingredient in becoming an effective mathematics problem-solver; it is equally important when facing real-life problems. Persistence and hard work can change failure into success.

We believe that being engaged in mathematical problem solving can potentially enhance children's mental wellbeing. If we consider the elements of the definition of wellbeing provided by the World Health Organization as *'the state in which an individual realises his or her own abilities',* and *'having positive self-image and esteem',* you will increasingly see these developing during your children's problem solving journey, supported by you.

During an intervention project we carried out with children aged 6-9 years, we were told by parents that mathematical problem solving helped their children not only to develop resilience, enjoyment and determination, but also with finding effective strategies to solve real-life challenges. It can also lead to higher self-esteem, motivation and a feeling of fulfilment. Other reported benefits include greater self-confidence and positive attitudes towards learning leading to higher achievement, not only in mathematics, but in other subjects too.

In real life, we are often faced with problems which need solving and require us to make decisions. Making decisions about what strategies to use in solving mathematical problems can train children's minds to make wiser decisions with more confidence.

One parent told us that her daughter, Natalie, found that she used her problem solving ideas to resolve disagreements with her classmates and, therefore, they contributed to her positive mental health and wellbeing. She said:

"Natalie would bring a real life problem or challenge home and we would discuss it using the same steps as we used with solving mathematics problems. What is

the problem, what do we know, what the different ways we can solve it are and then evaluate what may happen. I am sure that having these skills helps her to manage stressful situations."

Aswari, 10, told us that solving mathematical problems makes him happy and, according to his Dad, it improves his mood and wellbeing. Aswari, too, uses the strategies he uses in solving mathematics problems with his work in other subjects and real life situations. He told us 'thinking about a problem and solving it calms you down.'

What do you do if you get stuck or make mistakes?

Children and parents we have worked with have told us that after the initial anxiety of not knowing how to go about solving a mathematical problem, children start accepting that making mistakes is an important part of finally arriving at satisfactory solutions. Parents have a vital role in encouraging children to revise their strategies as they try different ideas and tell them that if things didn't go as planned it does not mean they have failed.

Adopting a problem solving strategy

A five step problem solving strategy and associated discussions were used in one household, which they believe helped their children to deal with other challenging situations and reduced anxiety both in school and at home. The list found a place on the kitchen noticeboard for immediate access when needed. The steps involved:

1. Ask: what is the problem?

2. Why is it a problem and why should you solve it?

3. List your ideas for solving the problem.

4. Discuss each idea asking how effective it is and cross out the ones which are not useful

5. Decide how you would act.

After acting on the solution, ideally, you would evaluate how successful the solution was and learn from it for future occasions.

Mathematics problem solving for building character and resilience

Based on interviews with parents who have been involved in mathematical problem solving with their children, we believe that problem solving does contribute to character-building; in particular, the traits of grit, curiosity, self-control, zest and optimism, as outlined in Paul Tough's (2013) book, *How Children Succeed: Grit, Curiosity, and the Hidden Power of Character.*

It may take time before your children learn to master the art of mathematical problem solving, but the experience may make them feel happier, and help them develop more self-confidence. They will also develop critical thinking and decision-making skills, more resilience and persistence. These attributes contribute towards higher achievement and general success. You will watch them grow in confidence and, in time, they will start recognising patterns and strategies they have used in previous problems to arrive at successful solutions.

Summary

Problem solving is an important aspect of learning mathematics. Everyone can become more proficient in problem solving and it can be a very enjoyable and stimulating experience. It can also help children's sense of wellbeing and character building.

Chapter 2

Problem solving in practice

The National Curriculum for Mathematics in England (DfE, 2013) lists its aims to ensure that all pupils:

- become **fluent** in the fundamentals of mathematics, including through varied and frequent practice with increasingly complex problems over time, so that pupils develop conceptual understanding and the ability to recall and apply knowledge rapidly and accurately

- **reason mathematically** by following a line of enquiry, conjecturing relationships and generalisations, and developing an argument, justification or proof using mathematical language

- can **solve problems** by applying their mathematics to a variety of routine and non-routine problems with increasing sophistication, including breaking down problems into a series of simpler steps and persevering in seeking solutions.

In order to achieve these aims we should develop pupils' numerical skills as well as mathematical reasoning. The National Curriculum stresses that pupils should be taught to apply arithmetic fluently to problems, understand and use measures, make estimates and check their work. They should be taught to apply their mathematics to both routine and non-routine problems, including breaking down more complex problems into a series of simpler steps. Parents have a vital role to play in helping children to develop these skills. In this Chapter we provide a set of helpful strategies and a range of examples of problems and the different approaches which can be applied to solve them.

Are the ideas of problem solving new?

The role of problem solving is an integral part of the learning and teaching of mathematics. This has been recognised for decades. More than three decades ago, the Cockcroft Report (1982) declared that '*problem solving is at the heart of mathematics*' and asserted that '*mathematics is only useful to the extent that it can be applied to a particular situation and that it is the ability to apply mathematics to a variety of situations to which we give the name problem solving'.* Since then, almost all the key official documents in England have emphasised the important role of problem solving in mathematics. For example, the Mathematics National Curriculum in England documents in 1989 and 2000 included the requirement of teaching problem solving, written in the 'Using and Applying' strand. The National Numeracy Strategy (1999), which has been a very influential document in the teaching of mathematics in England also had strongly emphasised the role of teaching problem solving to children. Finally, an analysis of both the national tests in mathematics and other standardised tests that schools use to assess children's mathematical learning requires children to solve problems, both to test mathematical content and the skills of thinking mathematically. Countries in the Far East which are often cited as high achievers in international mathematics tests encourage children to solve problems regularly and alongside the teaching of facts and skills.

The processes involved in problem solving

As part of a teachers' professional development programme Koshy (2003) tried to analyse the different aspects involved in problem solving; this was published in a Mathematics Co-ordinators' file by PfP. She found the outcomes very illuminating and useful and shared with both practising teachers and teacher-trainees. Here are some thoughts, which emerged from teachers and have much relevance for parents when they train children in problem solving skills. We discussed some benefits of encouraging children to become effective problem solvers in Chapter 1. Here are some more.

Problem solving in mathematics

- is an intellectual activity;

- involves the pursuit of solutions to problems which is highly satisfying and stimulating;

- requires logic, reasoning and systematic working;

- provides a strong framework in which some key skills learnt in the context of mathematics transfer to other learning;

- provides a natural context for training children to be effective problem solvers;

- can help to develop children's tenacity and confidence in doing mathematics;

- is described by brain-function researchers as a helpful strategy to enhance children's general capacity for learning.

Try these problems

Here are some practical problems which Koshy (2003) tried with teachers. Try them yourself; you may want to do these with your children or friends. Then try to analyse what is involved in solving each of the problems.

Problems

1. Mary has 106 marbles and John has 89. How many marbles have they altogether?

2. Emily had 366 stamps. She gave away a third of her stamps to her friend. How many has she left?

3. The area of a rectangular room is 168 square metres. Its perimeter is 52 metres. What are the length and width of the room?

4. The difference between two numbers is 37. The total of the two numbers is 217. What are the two numbers?

5. Natalie bought T-shirts for £13 each and some jumpers for £10 each. She spent a total of £105. How many of each did she buy?

Analysis of Strategies

These notes may help with your analysis, but there may be other strategies you may use. There are many approaches you can use in solving problems.

Problem 1 [Answer: 195]

This is a single step problem which can be solved by a single 'learnt' operation of adding the two numbers together. It involves the simple use of a procedure.

Problems 2 and 3 [Answer: 249 and 14m/12m]

These problems involve more than one step, but can be solved by employing more systematic use of rules, strategies and procedures. Problem 2, for example, requires two steps: finding a third of 366 and then subtracting that number from 366. Problem 3 requires an understanding of the concept of area and working with reasonable estimates of length and breadth and multiplying them to get 168, from which suitable measures are selected for the perimeter.

Problems 4 and 5 [Answers 127/90 and 5/4]

These require even more systematic estimating, reasoning and recording. Using tables can help. Here is one example of the strategy used by children to solve problem 5.

Number of jumpers	1	2	3	4	5	6	7
Cost of jumpers	10	20	30	40	50	60	70
Left-over money	95	85	75	65	55	45	35
Exact no. of T-shirts bought (without remainders)	–	–	–	5	–	–	–

Helpful steps in problem solving

- Read the question carefully.

- What is the problem asking you to find out?

- Read it again and a third time if you are not sure.

- What do you know? Make a list and notes, then organise them.

- What will help you? Draw a picture. Make a model. Draw a table. Talk it through with someone. Using practical materials can help.

- Work on the problem, keeping a record of what you are doing. What steps are you listing? Don't worry about scribbles and crossings out as all the really good mathematicians make mistakes. Your scribbles will help you to keep track of your progress and show an adult what you are thinking.

- Got an answer?

- Ask yourself – have I solved the problem? Is this what I was asked to do?

- Does the answer make sense? Is it realistic?

- Can you check the answer, using the given clues? Perhaps working backwards.

- Does the answer make sense? Does it feel right?

- Are there other solutions?

It is also useful to instil and reinforce the idea that:

Being stuck is OK, that is part of learning and becoming a successful mathematician.

Development of problem solving processes

As children progress through their problem solving sessions, they should be encouraged to develop the following processes which are useful for raising their confidence and achievement in mathematics. The processes are:

- Estimating

- Looking for patterns

- Reasoning

- Applying logic

- Working systematically

- Recording thoughts and steps

- Asking more questions

- Making hypotheses, making reasonable guesses and estimates

- Doubting

- Convincing

- Proving, working backwards to check.

Working together

The benefits of children working in groups or with adults are highlighted in research and theoretical literature. When children work with others they are likely to participate more actively and share ideas which in turn strengthen their conceptual understanding.

Recording work

It useful for children to keep a separate book or folder for problem solving. Encourage them to record their efforts. Failures should also be recorded as these often show both the children and the adults working with them where the children may need further guidance. Recordings also provide evidence of children's development in thinking and the use of more effective strategies. It is useful for children to record the strategies and procedures which they have used before.

In the following sections we provide you with a range of problems to solve. All of them encourage children to use logic and reasoning.

Let us now consider the types of problem solving we see in classrooms.

Word problems which follow specific operations

Koshy (2017) provides a useful discussion of different kinds of problems children encounter in school. Many textbooks provide problem solving exercises at the end of a section dealing with a specific operation. For example, the following are the type of problems often included at the end of the section on addition:

> *John has 4 marbles, he won 7 more. How many has he now?*
>
> *We have 12 writing books, 6 maths books and 13 word books. How many books are there altogether?*
>
> *Naomi had 34 stamps in one packet and 23 in another. How many does she have altogether?*

After the section on subtraction sums, the same textbook would have:

> *I had 12 sweets, I ate 6. How many have I left?*
>
> *There are 24 children in the class, 7 are away. How many children are present?*
>
> *Out of the 16 children who went to a concert, 4 were girls, how many were boys?*

It is unlikely that any child who works through these problems will have difficulty in deciding which operation to use as they are included within a specific context of number operations.

One important point to remember is how children choose an operation to solve a problem. This involves children often looking for 'clue words' in a problem to help them to select the appropriate operation. For example, if the word 'more' appears in the problem, they may consider it to be an 'addition' operation, 'share' being taken as the clue for 'division' and so on. For example, a child who had solved the problem: 'John had 46 marbles, Nadia had 58 marbles, how many more marbles did Nadia have than John?' added the two numbers because the word 'more' was in the problem. The word 'more' was used by the child as a clue for 'adding' the two numbers instead of finding the difference between the two numbers which will require the use of subtraction (58 − 46 = 12 more marbles).

Here are some examples of clues which may be interpreted wrongly by children. You may want to try this kind of problem with your children.

> Daniel has 8 cakes. He divided each cake into 4 pieces. How many pieces are there altogether?
>
> Ron has saved up £6 to buy a game. The game costs £15. How much more does he need?
>
> I have 16 stamps, my friend has 3 times as many. How many stamps do we have altogether?

Indeed, children need to spot what operations to use for solving word problems; but they need to make their decisions based on an understanding of what different operations mean. They need to make sense of the operations and what operations actually do to numbers. When asked 'if one bag contains 8 sweets and you had 6 bags of them, how many are there altogether?' a child may start adding 8 six times. Here you need to point out the fact that multiplication is in fact repeated addition which would result in the child internalising that principle and applying it in future situations.

There are two other types of problems – those which are **purely mathematical** and those which are **realistic**. Here is a problem and how a group of 9-year old children solved it.

Handshakes

> *If all 16 people in a room shook hands with each other once, how many handshakes will take place? What if there are 100 people? 1000 people? Can you work out a way of finding out the number of handshakes for any number of people?*

The handshakes problem is a mathematical problem that may not have a purpose in a real life context, but it provides an opportunity to work systematically, look for patterns and generalise. Any formulas arrived at may be useful in other similar situations and can often give children a kind of power.

A class teacher asked two groups of children to find out how many handshakes would take place at their tables with four children. The simple, first level of this problem enabled all children to participate and achieve successful outcomes. Various strategies could be used. For example, the children found:

- the solution for the number of handshakes for a small number of people could be found by drawing pictures or by actually shaking hands and counting the number of handshakes which actually took place;

As a second level, they

- worked systematically and used a table to record results to find out how many handshakes would take place.

In the second level, the children produced a table of results:

Number of children	Added Handshakes	Total handshakes
1	0	0
2	1	1
3	1 + 2	3
4	1 + 2 + 3	6
5	1 + 2 + 3 + 4	10
6	1 + 2 + 3 + 4 + 5	15

By spotting the way the sequence developed, they worked out that for seven people it would be 21, for eight people it will be 28, for nine people it will be 36 and for ten people the total number of handshakes will be 45. Working out the total number of handshakes for a larger number of people, using this method, some of them realised would be laborious. So, the teacher suggested, to those who she thought were capable of taking it further, that they looked for an easier way to work out the number of handshakes for a larger number of people. Is there a connection between the number of people and the number of handshakes? Could they spot a relationship? Some pupils were able to take up the challenge, established a rule and explained how they arrived at a generalisation as follows.

If there are n children (where n can be any number) the number of handshakes will be given by:

number of handshakes = $n(n-1)/2$

For example for 20 children, the number of handshakes will be $(20 \times 9) \div 2 = 190$

Realistic problems such as planning a 'value for money' holiday with £1500 using travel brochures, or planning to set up a school shop are more open-ended, and are unlike the structured mathematical problems which have 'set' solutions. The data for realistic problems are likely to be 'untidy and awkward'; this encourages children to select effective strategies and make adjustments. This kind of problem solving helps children to make sensible interpretations of results. Realising, for example, there can be no 'remainder people' or 'half people' and that it is impossible to buy 'fractions of stamps'. Realistic problems are also likely to develop more rational thinking and ways of making sense of operations, and of course more perseverance, which is all-important.

Examples of problems

Here are some problems for you to try. **Some notes and the solutions** to the problems are given at the end of the set of problems. **Don't look at the solutions before you try each of the problems! Let your children join in.**

Set 1. Finding a rule

Towers

The handshakes problem in the previous section leads to a generalisation and finding a rule. Here is a simpler one.

Build the first tower. It is two bricks tall. Now build the second tower. It is three bricks tall.

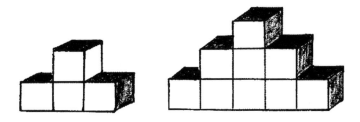

What if you were to build 2 more towers following the same rule. How many bricks would you need for each tower?

If you had 36 bricks, how many bricks tall will it be?

- What if you had 49 bricks?

- What if you had 81 bricks?

- What is special about the number of bricks used and the height of the tower?

Set 2. Puzzles

a.) Number Triangles

Write numbers in the circles so that each side has a total of 5. One has been done for you. Now try using bigger numbers 0-9 to get the same total on each side. Make numbers 0 to 9 on small sheets of paper to help you move them around. (You can use the same bits of paper to help you.) You can use the same number more than once. Some numbers may not be used at all. Write numbers in the circles so that each side has the same total.

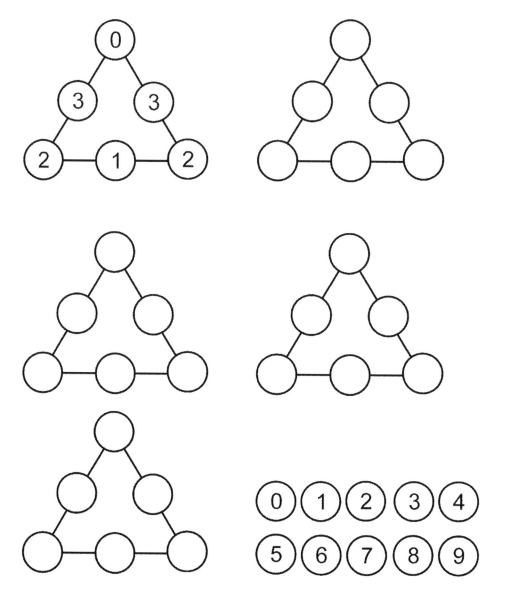

b.) Puzzle it out

The sum (total) of each row and column is given.

Each of the symbols in this grid represents a particular number.

Can you find out what they stand for?

Then fill in the missing number in the right hand corner.

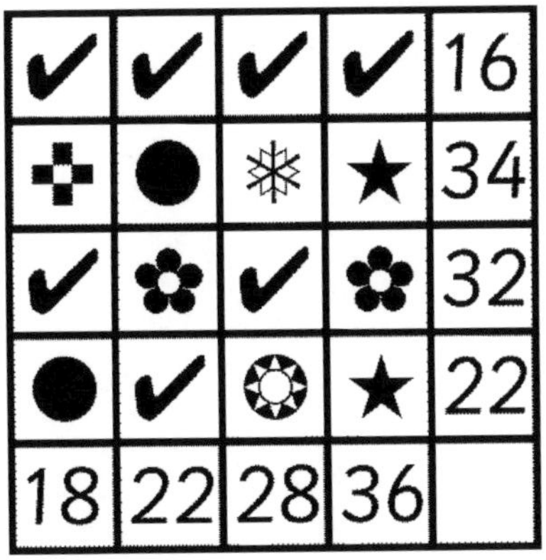

✔	✔	✔	✔	16
✛	●	❄	★	34
✔	✿	✔	❀	32
●	✔	✵	★	22
18	22	28	36	

Set 3: Finding the odd one out

Spot the odd one out

a) Millilitre   Kilometre   Kilolitre   Gallon

b) 50% $\dfrac{22}{44}$ 55   half

c) Centimetre   metre   kilometre   seconds   millimetre

d) 9   18   27   36   46

Set 4: Estimate

a) Which of the following is a reasonable weight of an orange?

6 grams   2 kilograms   200 grams

b) Which of the following lengths is a reasonable answer for the length of your classroom floor?

20 metres   1 kilometre   5 metres   16 centimetres

Set 5: Word problems

a) I bought 15 colour pens – each costing the same – for 90p.

How much did each pen cost?

b) How many coaches do we need to take all 360 of the children in the school to see a pantomime if each coach can take 50 children?

c) If you win a free holiday which gives you free travel for 1 million seconds, for how many days can you travel?

d) How many 10 millilitre glasses can be filled with 1 litre of orange juice?

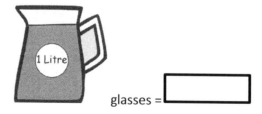

glasses =

e) Amanda, Azim and Alex are going to see a play. The total cost for their tickets is £39.15. How much does each ticket cost?

f) Belinda and her mother noticed that the cost of a blouse was half that of a pair of trousers and the cost of a pair of trousers was half the cost of a jacket. If they paid £154 in total how many of each did they buy?

g) If you want to be rich...

(i)   Would you rather have 10p a day pocket money for 2 weeks
        or

(ii)   A penny on the first day, double that on the second day, double that
        on the third day and so on for 2 weeks (14 days).

Set 6: Extended open ended problem

Furnish your dream bedroom

You have a chance to plan a dream bedroom. Use a catalogue, which shows items
of furniture and other luxuries. Floor covering and curtains will be in the room,
but you must choose a bed and any other items you wish to buy.

It is a good idea to discuss your idea with a friend before you decide what to buy
and where you will place everything.

Your total budget is £900, you can go over or under your budget by £50.

Make a list of the items you will buy and an approximate calculation of your total.
You can buy as many cuddly toys and pictures as you like. No calculators are
allowed at this stage.

You must also draw a plan (to scale) of your room
and where you will place all the items you will be
buying. Doors and windows are marked.

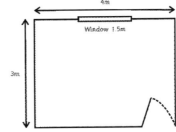

Set 7: Building number sense. What is my secret number?

a)   My secret number is even

?   It has two digits

?   It is between 20 and 40

?   If you count in fives you will land on this number

    ❓   If you add the two digits you get 3.

b)   My secret number is even.

    ❓   It has 2 digits.

    ❓   It is between 40 and 50.

    ❓   When you count up in twos you will land on this number.

    ❓   The two digits add up to 12.

Set 8: More problems involving length, time, capacity, money and weight

a)   The apple tree in our garden is 4 metres tall, the pear tree is 5 metres and 50 centimetres tall.

- Which tree is taller?

- How much taller is it?

b)   My birthday is on 12th August.
Today is 23rd July. How many days do I have to wait for my birthday?

c)   A bottle has 90 millilitres of medicine in it. If I have 15 millilitres of medicine a day, how many days will it last?

d)   My mother bought a 2 litre bottle of orange juice for my party. She says each plastic cup holds 100 millilitres. How many cups can we fill?

e)   I am raising money for a charity.

I bought a pack of 12 kilogram of biscuits for £10.50. I divided these into small packs of 200 grams and sold each pack for £2.25.

How much profit will I make?

f)   A turkey weighing 4 kilograms 500 gram.

To roast it, it takes 20 minutes per kilogram and then add another 20 minutes before you take it out of the oven.

How long will it take to roast a turkey?

Notes and solutions to problems

Set 1: Finding a rule

a) Towers

- If you had 36 bricks, your tower would be 6 bricks tall.

- If you had 81 bricks, your tower would be 9 bricks tall.

- If you continue to build towers of following the same pattern, you will see that the height of the tower is the square root of the total number of bricks.

    Or $2^2 = 4$ 1st tower

    $3^2 = 9$ 2nd tower

    $4^2 = 16$ bricks

    $5^2 = 25$ bricks

    $9^2 = 81$ bricks

    A tower which is 10 bricks tall will have $10^2 = 100$ bricks

    The number of bricks is the square of the height (in bricks)

    $10^2 = 100$ bricks.

Set 2:   Puzzle it out

a)   These are easy to check. See the example given.

b) Puzzle it out

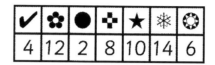

The bottom right hand corner total = 104

Set 3:   Finding the odd ones out

(These will need knowledge of measures, numbers, fractions and percentages to solve. Discuss this with the children.)

a)   Kilometre (measure of length, not a measure of volume)

b)   55 (not equal to half)

c)   Seconds (not a measure of length)

d)   46 (not a multiple of 3)

Set 4:   Estimate

a)   200 grams

b)   20 metres

Set 5:   Word problems

a)   6p each

b)   8 coaches, otherwise if you only had 7 coaches, 10 children would not be able to go to the pantomime.

c)   11 full days

d)   100 glasses

e)   £13.05

f)   Jackets = £88, pair of trousers = £44, one blouses = £22
There are other correct solutions.

g)   You would choose (ii)

Set 6: Furnish your dream bedroom

There are many solutions to this. You may wish to use a calculator to check the amounts within the budget.

Set 7: Building number sense

    a) 30

    b) 48

Set 8:

    a) Pear tree is taller. It is 1 metre and 50 centimetres taller.

    b) 20 days

    c) 6 days

    d) 20 bottles

    e) I can make 60 packs

        I get £2.25 x 60 = £135.00

        My profit is £124.50

    f) 110 minutes (1 hour and 50 minutes)

Summary

In this Chapter we discussed the processes involved in problem solving in mathematics. We introduced you to different types of problems to help children develop a range of ideas and methods.

Chapter 3

Starting problem solving at home

There are many opportunities at home to solve mathematical problems. You will also be able to have plenty of 'mathstalk' which is a key aspect of understanding mathematical ideas and applying them efficiently. This Chapter gives a number of activities that you can do at home with your child, without the need for special equipment. Most of the resources you need will be things you have around the house anyway, for example – a calculator, clock, tape measure, playing cards, dice etc. You will also have many opportunities to solve problems in real life during normal daily activities. Doing these together can be great fun.

A vital part of the problem solving process is the questions that you ask your child. Some suggestions are given in italics for each activity, but of course you may come up with alternative and better questions yourself.

1. Calculator

A basic calculator would be best, but if you don't have one, most phones and tablets have a calculator app.

Knowing how to use a calculator is a very useful skill in learning mathematics. We don't mean using a calculator to do your simple sums, but to use it for playing mathematical games and solving problems which involve long calculations (which take away the pleasure from the process of problem solving.) We give you some examples later in this section.

Let us start with some simple work using calculators, getting used to them.

"What are the four basic maths operations?"

The four operation signs are + (plus), - (minus). x (times) and ÷ (divide).

Ask your child to work out the answers to these sums and record the answers:

  8 + 4 =

  8 - 4 =

  8 x 4 =

  8 ÷ 4 =

Now do the same with the numbers the other way round:

  4 + 8 =

  4 - 8 =

  4 x 8 =

  4 ÷ 8 =

> *"Did you get the same answers? Try this again with a different pair of numbers and see what happens. Try to explain what you find out."*

Solution: With addition and multiplication, you will get the same answer when you switch the numbers round. With subtraction and division, you won't. The mathematical term for this is the COMMUTATIVE law of addition and multiplication.

Koshy (2017) provides some useful ideas for using calculators to encourage estimation and make sense of number operations.

Activities such as the 'Broken keys' provide excellent opportunities for children to think about the structure of numbers and analyse calculations.

A careful study of the two activities below will show how the calculator is instrumental in encouraging children to perform mental calculations, estimate and think about the structure of numbers. Activity 2, 'Six discrimination', also provides children with opportunities for developing reasoning, communicating, justifying and proving.

Activity 1 – Broken Keys

Only the following keys are working on your calculator.

Can you make the number 100, using just these keys?

Activity 2 – Six discrimination
(adapted from NCC, 1992)

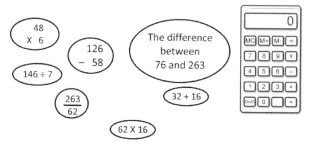

The ⁶ button on your calculator is broken.

♦ Find answers to the above and show your workings out.

♦ Work in pairs

♦ Share a calculator between two.

♦ You and your partner must agree before you DO the sum.

Try this:

If the product (multiplied) of two consecutive numbers (numbers next to each other) is 89700, what are the two numbers? [Answer: 299 and 300]

Here you are allowing calculators to do the hard work whilst children will be using the time in thinking, estimating, reasoning and mental arithmetic.

Now try these:

I divided a 2-digit number by another 2-digit number and the answer given by my calculator was 0.77777. What were the two numbers? Record how you did this.

You can use the calculator to see if you got the correct answers. One correct answer is 49 ÷ 63.

Activities such as 'Number Whiz', below, are designed to develop children's 'feel' for number by considering the size of numbers, analysing and exploring the nature of number operations, estimating approximate answers and developing sound strategies. If you look at the questions carefully, you can see how allowing children to use a calculator to check will release their mental energy so that they can do some real thinking about what is involved in number calculations. Thinking, estimating and analysing strategies are important processes for problem solving.

Number Whiz

You can only use the digits 1, 2, 3, 4, 5, 6 and each digit can be used once only. Using these digits see if you can obtain the following results:

The first one is done for you.

Can you make the answer 390?

Using 254 + 136 = you get 390

The biggest possible answer

☐☐☐ + ☐☐☐ =

The smallest answer

☐☐☐ – ☐☐☐ =

The smallest answer

☐☐☐ × ☐☐☐ =

The biggest answer

☐☐☐ × ☐☐☐ =

---

2. Calendar

Look at the calendar for this year.

> "How many months have 31 days?
>
> How many months have 30 days?
>
> There is one month that has less than 30 days. Which month is that?
>
> "The month that has less than 30 days is a special month, because it is the only one that does not always have the same number of days. See if you can find out more about it.
>
> "In each row the numbers up by one each time you move across.
>
> How much do the numbers go up in each column as you move down?
>
> [REMEMBER rows go ACROSS, columns go DOWN]
>
> "Why do you think this happens?" [The numbers go up by 7 because there are 7 days in a week.]
>
> "Find your birthday on the calendar. What day of the week will it be this year?
>
> Is it on the same day every year?
>
> "Now find the birthdays for other members of your family and friends, and tell them what day their birthdays will fall on."
>
> How long do you have to wait for your birthday? How many days? How many hours?

3. Five Dice

If you don't have dice at home, they are readily available in discount stores.

> "Roll the five dice together and add up all the dots. Do this at least 10 times and write down your scores."
>
> "What do you think is the highest score that you could get with 5 dice? What do you think is the lowest?"

Copy the table below and ask your child to fill in the numbers.

Number of dice	Highest possible score	Lowest possible score
1		
2		
3		
4		
5		
6		

[Highest possible scores are 6/12/18/24/30/36, and lowest possible scores are 1/2/3/4/5/6.]

> "Now look at just one dice. What number is opposite the 1? Opposite the 2? Opposite the 3? Can you see the pattern between the numbers that are opposite each other?

[The numbers on opposite faces always add up to 7].

> "You can use this pattern to do a trick. Ask someone to roll a dice. Then tell them immediately what the hidden number on the bottom is."

Using more dice you can ask:

Who can tell me how many spots there are, altogether, on one dice? 2 dice? 3 dice?

I am going to place one dice on top of the other, can you tell me what the hidden numbers are? What if I did this with three dice?

In how many different ways can you get number 6, or number 10, throwing two dice together?

4. Number Square

1	2	3	4	5	6	7	8	9	10
11	12	13	14	15	16	17	18	19	20
21	22	23	24	25	26	27	28	29	30
31	32	33	34	35	36	37	38	39	40
41	42	43	44	45	46	47	48	49	50
51	52	53	54	55	56	57	58	59	60
61	62	63	64	65	66	67	68	69	70
71	72	73	74	75	76	77	78	79	80
81	82	83	84	85	86	87	88	89	90
91	92	93	94	95	96	97	98	99	100

Your child may have a large copy of the number square from school. If not, you can easily buy one, or make your own.

"Use your big copy of the number square for these questions.

*Remember that **ROWS** go **ACROSS** and **COLUMNS** go **DOWN**."*

"Find the 4 in the top row. Follow down the column with your finger. By how much are the numbers getting bigger each time? Try this again starting with a different number."

[Numbers go up by 10.]

"Now start at the number 1 and follow the diagonal across the square to 100 with your finger. By how much are the numbers getting bigger each time?

[Numbers go up by 11]

"Now start at the number 10 and follow the other diagonal across the square to 91 with your finger. By how much are the numbers getting bigger each time?"

[Numbers go up by 9]

"All the numbers in the 2 times table are in five columns. Can you find them?"

[Columns starting with 2, 4, 6, 8 and 10]

"All the numbers in the 5 times table are in two columns. Can you find them?"

[Columns starting with 5 and 10]

"See how many other patterns you can find in the numbers in the square".

5. Snakes and ladders

If you don't have a Snakes and Ladders board, you can probably find one in a Charity Shop.

Play the game several times. Remember to go UP the ladders and DOWN the snakes.

"Look at the ladders and write down which square each one starts at and which square it finishes at. Can you work out how many squares each ladder sends you up?"

Starting square	Finishing square	How many squares does it send you up?

"Now look at the snakes and write down the starting square and finishing square for each one. Can you work out how many squares each snake sends you down?"

Starting square	Finishing square	How many squares does it send you down?

Can you make up your own Snakes and Ladders game and make up your own rules?

6. Tape Measure

If you don't have a tape measure, you can buy one very cheaply from a discount store.

"The tape measure has two sides. Can you see why?"

[One side is for measuring in **inches** and the other side is for measuring in **centimetres** (cm for short).]

"When you are measuring you must always start at zero, which is the very end of the tape. Measure these objects first using inches and then using centimetres."

Object	Length in inches	Length in cm
Book		
Your foot		
Table (height)		
Door (width)		
Cereal packet		
Television		
Mobile phone		
Lunchbox		
Bed		

"Looking at your table, can you work out about how many cm make one inch? [It's between two whole numbers.]

[2.5cm make 1 inch]

"Now measure your height and the height of an adult in your family. The best way to do this is to stand with your back flat against a wall, and get someone to mark in pencil where the top of your head is. Then you can use the tape measure.

"Height is usually given in feet and inches or metres. Can you find out how to change from inches to feet and to change from centimetres to metres?

[Hint: There are 12 inches in a foot and 100 cm in a metre.]

People say that the length of your arm is three times the length around your head. Is this true?

7. Ten Cards

You need a pack of playing cards for this activity. Again, you can buy them very cheaply at discount stores.

Take the pack of playing cards and remove the picture cards (four Jacks, four Queens and four Kings) and the jokers, if there are any. The aces count as ones.

> *"There are four different suits in the pack: hearts, diamonds, clubs and spades. Do you know which one is which?"*

Shuffle the cards and place 8 of them face up on the table. Keep the rest in your hand.

> *"Can you see two cards that add up to 10?"*

[For example 1 (ace) and 9, 2 and 8, 3 and 7, 4 and 6; or you are allowed 10 on its own.]

Place two more cards from the pack in your hand to cover the card or cards that make 10. Ask again:

> *"Can you see two cards that add up to 10?"*

Continue until all the cards have been used. Sometimes it is not possible. Try again.

[This is an excellent activity to reinforce number bonds to 10, which form the basis for addition and subtraction.]

8. My Day in a Pie Chart

> *"Choose a day at the weekend or in the school holidays. Note down everything you do for the whole 24 hours and how long each activity takes. Put your results in a table. Some of the rows in the table have been left blank for you to fill in."*
>
> *"When you have finished a whole day, draw and colour in the pie chart below to show how you spent your day. How many hours are there in a day? So how many sections should your pie chart be split into?"*

[Each section of the chart represents one hour, so the pie chart should have 24 sections. If this is too difficult to draw, you could draw a bar chart instead.]

Activity	How many hours
Sleeping	
Eating	
Watching television	
Playing with friends	
Playing on computer	
Reading	
Drawing	
Helping with chores	

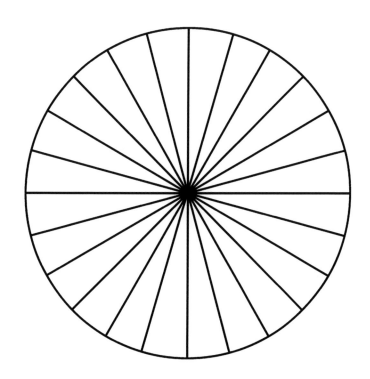

9. Weather

To answer these questions, you will have to look in one or more of the following places:

- Newspaper, magazines and books

- The Internet

Temperature

Where is the hottest place you can find in the world? What is the temperature there?	
Where is the coldest? What is the temperature there?	
What is the difference in temperature between the two?	
What is the temperature in London?	

Rainfall

Where is the wettest place you can find in the world? What is the average annual rainfall?	
Where is the driest place? What is the average annual rainfall?	
What is the average annual rainfall in England?	

10. Your dream holiday

Pick up a holiday brochure from a Travel Agent.

"Choose one place where you would like to go on holiday. See if you can answer these questions using the information in the brochure."

Where is the place you have chosen for your holiday?	
How much would it cost for your family to go at the cheapest time of year?	
How much would it cost at the most expensive time of year?	
Which airport would you fly from?	
What time of day is the flight?	
What is the average temperature at the hottest time of year?	
What is the currency in this country?	
What is the exchange rate (how much is £1 in the local currency)?	

11. Breakfast cereals

Find two different packets of cereal that you have in your house.

" Look at the information printed on the sides of the packets and see if you can copy and fill in the table below, using the typical values for 100g of the cereal."

Cereal name		
Energy		
Protein		
Carbohydrate		
Fat		
Fibre		
Sodium		

"Do you know which of these things are good for you and which are bad? If you can find out, then decide which is the healthiest breakfast cereal."

"You will also find a list of the vitamins and minerals present in the cereals. Most of these have letters (e.g. Vitamin D). How many different letters can you find?"

The remaining three activities in this chapter are 'out and about' activities rather than ones to do at home.

12. At the supermarket

	Cheapest	Most expensive	Difference in price
Tin of baked beans			
Large sliced loaf of bread			
1 litre carton of orange juice			
Pot of raspberry jam			

You will need to supply your child with a notebook and pen for this visit to the supermarket.

> *"Look for these items on the shelves. Can you find the cheapest and the most expensive brand of each item and write them in the table."*

> *"Now work out the difference in prices for each item and write it in the last column.*

> *"Suppose you eat one tin of baked beans a week. How many is that in a year? How much would you save in a year by buying the cheapest?*

> *"Do the same for the other items."*

13. At the library

> *"Can you estimate (that means guess) the number of books in the library?"*

> *"Now ask the Librarian how many books there really are. Were you close?*

> *"Now choose two books from the Children's section – a picture book for babies and a first reading book.*

> *"For each book, count up approximately (that means you don't have to be exact) how many words on each page. Then look at the number of the last page in the book. Fill in the numbers in the table.*

	Number of words on a page	Number of pages in the book	Total number of words
Picture book			
First reading book			

> *"Can you see how to work out the total number of words in each book? You may need a calculator to work this out."*

14. At the bus stop

Go to a bus stop near where you live.

> *"Look at the timetable. This gives you lots of information about the buses that stop there."*
>
> *"How many buses come to this bus stop?"*
>
> *"Write down the numbers of all the buses."*
>
> *"Now choose just one of the bus numbers. Can you answer these questions?"*

What time is the earliest bus?	
What time is the latest bus?	
Where does the bus start?	
Where does the bus finish?	

15. Word games

Playing word games provide many opportunities for mathematical thinking and reasoning.

Example of a word game:

My secret number is:

between 1 and 100

It is bigger than 50

It is a square number

It is a multiple of 4

It is nearer to 70 than it is to 100

What is my number?   [Answer: 64]

Children can be encouraged to make up their own examples.

16. Problem solving from stories

Stories provide many opportunities for problem solving. For example, think about the story of Goldilocks and the Three Bears. There are many examples of problems you can ask children to solve.

Here are some examples:

How many bowls of porridge do you need if the bear family had 5 visitors?

Can you design a new house for the bears with a fence and a lock so that people can't just walk in?

Can you plan a picnic for the bear family and find out how much it would cost?

Summary

In this Chapter we discussed the many possibilities for problem solving both within and outside your home. These problems provide many opportunities for mathematical talk and for the development of logic, reasoning and applying mathematical ideas.

Chapter 4

Problem solving and reasoning questions to try

Here are some problems for you to try with your children. They are grouped according to the level of challenge, easy to harder.

Set A

1. I am thinking of two numbers. If I add them together it makes 9. If I multiply them, it makes 20. What are my two numbers?

2. You have four number cards marked with the numbers 1, 3, 5 and 6. How many different totals can you make using two numbers at a time? What about if you use three numbers at a time?

3. This is a number sequence: 3, 6, 9, 12, 15, … Do you recognise this pattern? What are the next three numbers?

4. Look at a dice. What number is opposite 1? What is opposite 2? What is opposite 3? Can you see a pattern in the pairs of opposite numbers?

5. You have 5 coins: 1p, 2p, 5p, 10p and 20p. How many different totals can you make?

6. You can choose from these four numbers: 1, 2, 4 and 8. Pick two numbers and add them together. Write down the answer. Try another two numbers. How many different answers can you get?

7. Sadie buys a bar of chocolate for 53p and a packet of sweets for 45p. How much does she spend?

8. Isaac is saving up to buy a computer game. It costs £15. He has already saved £8. How much more does he need?

9. Izzy needs to score 12 with three dice. Her first two throws are 3 and 5. What does she need to score with the third dice?

10. Callum buys two pens for 35p each. He pays with a pound coin. How much change does he get?

Set B

1. Can you guess the mystery number from these clues:

   The number is even

   It has two digits

   It is between 40 and 50

   The two digits add up to 12

2. Draw three circles on a sheet of paper.

   You have the number 1, 2, 3, 4, 5, 6, 7, 8 and 9.

   Can you place three numbers in each circle so that the total in each circle is 15?

3. Look at this sequence of numbers:

   5, 10, 15, 20, 25, ...

   Can you say what the next three numbers would be? And can you say why?

4. You have these numbers:

   5   4   1   7

   What is the biggest number you can make? What about the smallest?

   What is the biggest even number you can make? And the smallest even number?

5. Ben bought a lollipop for 6p. He paid for it exactly. Which coins did he use? There are five different ways to do this. How many can you find?

   What if the lollipop cost 7p?

6. Charlie works as a shelf filler at Fresco supermarket. He is stacking tins of baked beans. Each tin has to be supported by two tins underneath, so the shape of the display is always a triangle.

   For example, if he builds a pile with three tins on the bottom, he has a total of 6 tins in the pile.

   By drawing different sized piles, can you work out the total number of tins for each one? Can you spot a pattern in these numbers?

Width of pile	1	2	3	4	5	6	7	8	9	10
Number of tins in pile										

7. The ice-cream man has several different flavours of ice-cream and sells double cones with two scoops of ice-cream in them.

   If you can only choose two flavours – vanilla and chocolate – how many different cones could you buy?

   What if you can choose from three flavours – vanilla, chocolate and strawberry? Can you draw and colour all the different cones?

8. Would you rather get paid for doing errands for a week:

   1p on the first day, 2p on the second day, 4p on the third day, and so on (doubling each time)

   Or:

   16p each day for 7 days?

9. If 8 taxis arrive at a party each carrying 5 passengers, how many guests arrive?

10. Twelve people came to watch the school show and they paid £5 each. How much were the ticket sales altogether?

Set C

1. What is a number between 30 and 40 that is a multiple of 4 and also a multiple of 6?

2. I am thinking of a shape. It is a quadrilateral with one line of symmetry and no parallel sides. What is it?

3. Here is a sequence of numbers.

    4, 11, 18, 25, 32, ...

    Can you say the next two numbers? What about the tenth number?

    What is the rule for the number pattern?

4. Coloured bricks are stacked in a pattern to make a tower.

| green |
| blue |
| red |
| green |
| blue |
| red |
| green |
| blue |
| red |

Can you work out the colour of the top brick if the tower is 100 bricks high?

5   Small apples cost 8p each and large apples cost 13p each. I buy some of each and spend exactly £1. How many of each size did I buy?

6. Four children took a test at school. There were 20 questions in the test. They scored 2 points for each correct answer, but lost a point for an incorrect answer. They had to answer all the questions.

    The table shows their scores. Can you work out how many questions each pupil got right and how many they got wrong?

Name	Score	Number of correct answers	Number of incorrect answers
Shanti	28		
David	13		
Lizzie	34		
Abu	37		

7. Andy bought 12 packets of fruit chews and gave a quarter of them to his little brother. If each packet had 8 sweets, how many sweets did Andy still have?

8. I need to cook 16 potatoes in the microwave. I have already cooked 7. If each potato takes 5 minutes to cook, how long will it take to cook the rest?

9. A farmer has 6 sacks of potatoes weighing 7kg, 10kg, 14kg, 23kg, 37kg and 49kg. How should he distribute these sacks onto his donkey so that the weight is evenly distributed on each side?

10. A carpenter is making 5 stools and 7 tables.

    Each stool has 3 legs and each table has 4 legs.

    How many legs will he need to make altogether?

Set D

1. Using the numbers 1 to 16 once only, complete this magic square so that each of the columns, rows and diagonals add up to 34.

	1	4	
7			6
9			12
	15	14	

2. Charlie has as many brothers as sisters. His sister Rosie has twice as many brothers as sisters. How many children are there in the family?

3. Look at this number sequence:

   14, 10, 6, 2, ...

   What are the next three numbers? What is the rule for finding the next number?

4. How many square numbers are there between 1 and 100?

    Can you write them all down? You can include 1 and 100.

5. Consecutive numbers are ones that are next to each other in order.
    Examples of sums adding consecutive numbers are:

    $$6 = 1 + 2 + 3$$
    $$9 = 4 + 5$$

    Is it possible to make every number from 1 to 20 using sums of consecutive numbers?

    Some numbers can be made by more than one consecutive sum, for example:

    $$15 = 7 + 8$$
    $$15 = 4 + 5 + 6$$
    $$15 = 1 + 2 + 3 + 4 + 5$$

    Which numbers cannot be made from consecutive numbers?

    What is special about these numbers?

    Can you predict the next numbers that can't be made?

6. The area of a rectangle is 24 square centimetres.

    How many different sized rectangles can you find with this area?

    What if the sides do not have to be whole numbers?

7. Rida's Mum spent £21 on drinks for Rida's birthday party. If the cola she bought was twice the price of the squash, and the lemonade was half the price of the squash, how much did she spend on each drink?

8. Fatima has a one-litre bottle of milk.

    She uses 25ml of milk to make one cup of tea.

    How many cups of tea can she make?

9. There are 500 books in Ms. Brooks' classroom.

    Half of them are storybooks.

    Three fifths of the storybooks have pictures.

    What percentage of all the books in the classroom have pictures?

10. These are the ingredients to make 12 fairy cakes.

    2 eggs

    300g of sugar

    200g of flour

    150g of butter

    Joe wants to make 30 cakes. How much of each of the ingredients will he need?

Set E

1. When my mother was 40, I was 16. Now she is twice as old as I am. How old am I now?

2. Using six 1's and any mathematical symbols, write a sum that has the answer 12.

3. Look at this number sequence:

   1, 1, 2, 3, 5, 8, 13, 21, ...

   Can you work out the next three numbers? What is the rule for finding the next number?

4. Can you fit the numbers 1 to 9 in the right places in this grid?

	Odd	Even	Multiple of 3
Prime			
Square			
Factor of 168			

5. A circle has 12 points on its circumference, all equally spaced. If each point is to be joined once to each of the other points, how many lines are needed?

6. In a Maths test, no two pupils scored the same. Brian scored less than 4 and Julie scored more than 6, but did not get full marks. Simon's score was the sum of Brian's and David's. Rachel scored three times as many as Brian. Brian, Julie and Rachel all scored even numbers, while Simon's and David's scores were both odd. David's score was half of Rachel's.

   What did each pupil score out of 10?

7. Use this train timetable to answer the questions below.

Starville	08:47	09:17	09:47	10:17
Harton	10:05	10:35	11.05	11:35
Sunnytown	10:17	10:47	11.17	11.47
Bridgetown	10:32	11:02	11:32	12:02
Twickton	10:45	11:15	11:45	12:15
Torbridge	11:02	11:32	12:02	12:32

Ahmed lives in Harton. He needs to be at Twickton by 11:30. What is the latest train he can catch?

Jamila lives in Starville. She catches the 09:47 train. How long will it take her to get to Torbridge?

8. Joe made three different stacks of wooden blocks.

The first stack was 4 blocks high, the second was double the size of the first, and the third was 10 blocks higher than the second.

How many blocks did Joe use altogether?

9. When I say two numbers, Jack adds them and Jill multiplies them. If Jack's answer is 10 and Jill's is 16, what are the two numbers? If Jack's answer is 15 and Jill's answer is 56, what are the two numbers? And what are the two numbers if Jack's answer is 31 and Jill's is 210?

10. When I looked out of my window one morning I could see some squirrels and some birds in the garden. Altogether I counted 22 heads and 72 feet.

How many squirrels and how many birds were there?

Set A guidance and solutions to problems

1. Ask: *"Let's think of all the number pairs that add up to 9"*. These are 1 and 8, 2 and 7, 3 and 6, 4 and 5. (If your child goes on to say 5 and 4, 6 and 3, 7 and 2, 8 and 1, point out that for example 4 + 5 gives the same answer as 5 + 4.). Then work out the multiplications (1 x 8 = 8, 2 x 7 =14, 3 x 6 = 18, 4 x 5 = 20) and you have the answer: 4 and 5.

   Note: When you add two numbers together, this is called the SUM.

   When you multiply, this is called the PRODUCT.

2. Say, *"We must be careful not to miss out any possible pairs"*. So use a systematic approach, beginning with all number pairs starting with 1, then all starting with 3, and so on.

   This gives:

1 + 3 = 4	3 + 5 = 8
1 + 5 = 6	3 + 6 = 9
1 + 6 = 7	5 + 6 = 11

   Remember that we don't need to do 3 + 1 as it gives the same answer as 1 + 3.

   Using three numbers at a time, we get:

   1 + 3 + 5 = 9

   1 + 3 + 6 = 10

   3 + 5 + 6 = 14

3. This is the three times table (just adding on 3 each time to get the next number). So the next three numbers are 18, 21 and 24.

4. On a dice the 6 is opposite to the 1, the 5 is opposite to the 2, and the 4 is opposite to the 3.

   What do these number pairs have in common – 1 and 6, 2 and 5, 3 and 4?

   The answer is that they all add up to 7. So by looking at the top number on a dice, you can guess the bottom (hidden) number. This is a good trick for your child to play on someone.

5. Use actual coins if you can. Again, use a systematic approach to make sure you have all the answers.

The different totals are:

1p	20p
2p	21p (1p + 20p)
3p (1p + 2p)	22p (2p + 20p)
5p	23p (1p + 2p + 20p)
6p (1p + 5p)	25p (5p + 20p)
7p (2p + 5p)	26p (1p + 5p + 20p)
8p (1p + 2p + 5p)	27p (2p + 5p + 20p)
10p	28p (1p + 2p + 5p +20p)
11p (1p + 10p)	30p (10p + 20p)
12p (2p + 10p)	31p (1p + 10p + 20p)
13p (1p + 2p + 10p)	32p (2p + 10p + 20p)
15p (5p +10p)	33p (1p + 2p + 10p + 20p)
16p (1p + 5p +10p)	35p (5p + 10p + 20p)
17p (2p + 5p + 10p)	36p (1p + 5p + 10p + 20p)
18p (1p + 2p + 5p +10p)	37p (2p + 5p + 10p + 20p)
	38p (1p + 2p + 5p + 10p + 20p)

6. Do the smallest ones first and then work up to make sure you don't miss any out. The different answers are:

3 (1 + 2)
5 (1 + 4)
6 (2 + 4)
9 (1 + 8)
10 (2 + 8)
12 (4 + 8)

7. *What word gives us a clue to tell us whether we should add or subtract?*

The word **and** means we should **add**.

So the answer is 53p + 45p = 98p.

8. *What word gives us a clue to tell us whether we should add or subtract?*

    The word here is **more,** which means we should **subtract**.

    So £15 – £8 gives us the answer £7.

9. This is a two-step problem, with two different calculations.

    Look for the key word for the first calculation. The word is **and** which tells us to **add**. So we do 3 + 5 = 8. For the second calculation there isn't really a key word, but we need to find out how much **more** she needs to score, so we **subtract**

    12 – 8 = 4.

10. This is another two-step problem. For the first part, the key words are **two** and **each**, which tells us to **multiply** 2 x 35p = 70p.

    The key word for the second step is **change**. This always means **subtract**. So we do £1 – 70p = 30p.

Set B guidance and solution to problems

1. From the first three clues, the possible numbers are 42, 44, 46 and 48.

    Using the fourth clue, the answer must be 48.

2. Take the first, last and middle numbers 1, 9 and 5 to make 15.

    Then you have 2, 6 and 7; and finally 3, 4 and 8.

3. The next three numbers are 30, 35 and 40.

    You could either think of the pattern as adding on 5 each time, or as the 5 times table. Either is correct.

4. The biggest number is 7541. You want the biggest digits in the most "powerful" positions (from the left, thousands, hundreds, tens and units).

    The smallest is 1457. Here you want the smallest digits in the most powerful positions.

    The biggest even number is 7514 and the smallest is 1574. An even number must have one of the digits 0, 2, 4, 6 or 8 in the units position.

5. You can make 6p in five ways:

    1p + 1p + 1p + 1p + 1p + 1p   1p + 1p + 1p + 1p + 2p

    1p + 1p + 2p + 2p   2p + 2p + 2p   1p + 5p

You can make 7p in six ways: add 1p to all the above, plus the extra one 2p/5p.

6. The pattern is that each time you are adding on one more than the time before. So you are adding 1, then 2, then 3, then 4, and so on. This sequence is called "triangle numbers" because it makes a pattern of triangles.

Width of pile	1	2	3	4	5	6	7	8	9	10
Number of tins in pile	1	3	6	10	15	21	28	36	45	55

7. You can make six different cones with three flavours:

> vanilla and vanilla
>
> chocolate and chocolate
>
> strawberry and strawberry
>
> vanilla and chocolate
>
> vanilla and strawberry
>
> chocolate and strawberry

8. If you chose the first way, at the end of 7 days you would get:

> 1p + 2p + 4p + 8p + 16p + 32p + 64p = 127p (or £1.27)

If you chose the second way, you would get 7 x 16p = 112p (or £1.12).

So the first way is better. (Most people guess wrong on this one.)

9. The key word here is **each**, which tells us to multiply. So the answer is 8 x 5 = 40.

10. The key word again is **each**, telling us to multiply. So we do 12 x £5 = £60.

Set C guidance and solution to problems

1. Multiples of 4 between 30 and 40 are 32, 36 and 40.

    Multiples of 6 are 30 and 36.

    So the answer must be 36, which is the only number in both sets.

2. It is a kite.

3. The next two numbers are 39 and 46.

    The tenth number is 67.

    The pattern is 'add 7 each time'.

4. The numbers of the red bricks are 1, 4, 7, and so on.

    The numbers of the blue bricks are 2, 5, 8, and so on.

    The numbers of the green bricks are 3, 6, 9, and so on.

    These numbers are all going up in threes. The numbers of the green bricks are actually the three times table (multiples of three). 99 is a multiple of 3 and so the 99th brick is green, so the 100th is red.

5. You can solve this by trial and error.

    Try different numbers of large apples, then see if what is left of the £1 is divisible by 8.

    One large apple is 13p, leaving 87p. 87 does not divide by 8.

    Two large apples are 26p, leaving 74p. 74 does not divide by 8.

    Three large apples are 39p, leaving 61p. 61 does not divide by 8.

    Four large apples are 52p, leaving 48p. 48 does divide by 8 (48 ÷ 8 = 6), so the answer is 6 small apples and 4 large ones.

6. Consider every possible score starting at 40 (all correct) in order to fill in the answer chart.

Name	Score	Number of correct answers	Number of incorrect answers
Shanti	28	16	4
David	13	11	9
Lizzie	34	18	2
Abu	37	19	1

You need to fill in the following chart first.

Score	Number of correct answers	Number of incorrect answers
40	20	0
37	19	1
34	18	2
31	17	3
28	16	4
25	15	5
22	14	6
19	13	7
16	12	8
13	11	9

7. A quarter of 12 is 3, so Andy still has 9 packets.

    If each packet has 8 sweets, Andy has 8 x 9 = 72 sweets.

8. If I have already cooked 7 potatoes, I have 16 – 7 = 9 potatoes left to cook.
    Each potato takes 5 minutes to cook, so it will take 9 x 5 = 45 minutes.

9. Add up the weights of all 6 sacks.

    $$7 + 10 + 14 + 23 + 37 + 49 = 140$$

    Half of 140 is 70, so we must arrange for 70kg to be on each side.

    If we take the lightest and the heaviest, we have 7 + 49 = 56, and 70 – 56 = 14.

    So we have 7kg, 14kg and 49kg on one side; 10kg, 23kg and 37kg on the other.

10. The 5 stools need 5 x 3 = 15 legs.

    The 7 tables need 7 x 4 = 28 legs.

    So altogether the carpenter will need to make 15 + 28 = 43 legs.

Set D guidance and solution to problems

1. Look at the bottom row first. 15 + 14 = 29 and 34 − 29 = 5, so the two bottom corners must be 2 and 3 (1 and 4 have already been used). If you try 3 in the bottom LH corner and 2 in the bottom RH corner, it makes the two missing numbers in the top row 15 and 14, which have already been used. So swap them round, which gives 16 and 13 in the two top corners. You can then fit the missing numbers 5, 8, 10 and 11 in the middle.

16	1	4	13
7	10	11	6
9	8	5	12
2	15	14	3

2. If Charlie has one brother and one sister, then Rosie has two brothers and no sisters.

   If Charlie has two brothers and two sisters, then Rosie has three brothers and one sister.

   If Charlie has three brothers and three sisters, then Rosie has four brothers and two sisters, which is the correct solution.

   So there are seven children in the family.

3. The next three numbers are -2, -6 and -10.

   The rule is: subtract 4 from the previous number.

4. A square number is formed by multiplying a number by itself.

   So the sequence of square numbers is:

1 (1 x 1)	36 (6 x 6)
4 (2 x 2)	49 (7 x 7)
9 (3 x 3)	64 (8 x 8)
16 (4 x 4)	81 (9 x 9)
25 (5 x 5)	100 (10 x 10)

5. These are the ones that can be made:

(1)	$11 = 5 + 6$
(2)	$12 = 3 + 4 + 5$
$3 = 1 + 2$	$13 = 6 + 7$
(4)	$14 = 2 + 3 + 4 + 5$
$5 = 2 + 3$	$15 = 7 + 8$
$6 = 1 + 2 + 3$	(16)
$7 = 3 + 4$	$17 = 8 + 9$
(8)	$18 = 3 + 4 + 5 + 6$
$9 = 4 + 5$	$19 = 9 + 10$
$10 = 1 + 2 + 3 + 4$	$20 = 2 + 3 + 4 + 5 + 6$

    So the ones that can't be made are 1, 2, 4, 8 and 16, i.e. doubling each time. So the next ones will be 32, 64, and so on.

6. The area of a rectangle is found by multiplying the base by the height.

    So we are looking for all pairs of numbers that multiply to make 24 (factor pairs of 24).

    These are: 1 and 24, 2 and 12, 3 and 8, 4 and 6.

    If we can use fractions and decimals, we could also do 0.5 x 48, 0.4 x 60, 0.2 x 120, and so on.

7. This is all about ratio.

    Lemonade is the cheapest drink, so we call that one part of our ratio.

    Squash is twice as much as lemonade, so that's two parts.

    Cola is twice as much as squash, so that's four parts.

    So our ratio is 1 : 2 : 4.

    $1 + 2 + 4 = 7$ and £21 ÷ 7 = £3, so she spent £3 on lemonade, £6 on squash, and £12 on cola.

8. There are 1000ml in one litre.

    We need to know how many lots of 25ml we can get from 1000ml.

    $1000 \div 25 = 40$.

    So she can make 40 cups of tea.

9. Half of 500 is 250.

    Three fifths of 250 is $250 \div 5 \times 3 = 150$.

150 out of 500 is the same as 30 out of 100 (dividing each number by 5), which is 30%.

10. We have the ingredients for 12 cakes, and we need to adapt for 30 cakes.

We can make 30 by doing two lots of 12 (24) plus a half of 12 (6).

So we need:

Eggs: 4 + 1 = 5

Sugar: 600g + 150g = 750g

Flour: 400g + 100g = 500g

Butter: 300g + 75g = 375g

Set E guidance and solution to problems

1. The difference between my age and my mother's is 40 − 16 = 24.

    This difference will always be the same.

    24 x 2 = 48, so I am now 24 and she is 48.

2. There are lots of different ways to do this.

    Here are a few:

    $$(1 \times 1 \times 1 \times 1) + 11 = 12$$
    $$(11 \times 1) + 1 - 1 + 1 = 12$$
    $$(1 \times 1) + 11 - 1 + 1 = 12$$

3. The next three numbers are 34, 55 and 89.

    The rule is: add two numbers to make the next term.

    This is a very famous sequence of numbers called the Fibonacci sequence.

4. Do the prime numbers first. 2 is the only even prime number, and 3 is the only prime number that is a multiple of 3. The odd prime could be 5 or 7, but 5 won't fit in anywhere else.

    The only square numbers between 1 and 9 are 1, 4 and 9, so they have to go in the second row.

	Odd	Even	Multiple of 3
Prime	5	2	3
Square	1	4	9
Factor of 168	7	8	6

    Then you are left with 6, 7 and 8 to fit in the bottom row.

5. Each of the 12 points is joined to all 11 others, making 12 x 11 = 132 lines.

    However by doing this, we are counting each line twice (once from each end), so we need to halve this number.

    $$132 \div 2 = 66$$

6. Look at Brian first. He scored less than 4 and an even number, so he must have scored 2.

    Rachel scored three times as many as Brian, so she scored 2 x 3 = 6.

    David's score was half Rachel's, so he must have scored 3.

    Simon's score was the sum of Brian's and David's, so he scored 2 + 3 = 5.

Julie scored more than 6 and less than 10, and her score was even, so it must have been 8.

So the scores were: Brian 2, David 3, Simon 5, Rachel 6, Julie 8.

7. Ahmed must catch the 10:35 train from Horton.

It will take Jamila 2 hours and 15 minutes.

The best way to work this out is:

> 09:47 to 10:00 is 13 minutes.
>
> 10:00 to 12:00 is two hours.
>
> 12:00 to 12:02 is 2 minutes.

Adding all those together gives 2 hours and 15 minutes.

8. The first stack was 4 blocks high.

The second was double the first, so it was 4 x 2 = 8 blocks high.

The third was 10 blocks higher than the second, so it was 8 + 10 = 18 blocks high.

So the total number of blocks was 4 + 8 + 18 = 30.

9. Firstly, we want two numbers that add to 10 and multiply to 16. They must be 2 and 8.

For the second problem, the numbers must be 7 and 8.

Thirdly, the numbers must be 10 and 21.

10. The answer is 8 birds and 14 squirrels.

The best way to solve this is 'trial and improvement'.

Just make a guess to start with: say 10 birds.

There must be a total of 22 creatures altogether (there are 22 heads), so if there are 10 birds then there must be 12 squirrels.

This gives a total of (10 x 2) + (12 x 4) = 68 legs, which is not quite enough, so next we need to try less birds and more squirrels, which will give us more legs.

Chapter 5

Conclusions

In the first two Chapters of this book we provided you with a background to the idea of problem solving and some useful strategies to help develop your children's problem solving skills. We discussed a list of steps which will enable children to become efficient in solving problems. A range of mathematical problems which children encounter in schools were provided, along with methods for solving them, as well as the solutions. The benefits of problem solving were also discussed.

In Chapter 3 we discussed how you can make problem solving part of your daily life, providing plenty of opportunities for 'Mathematical Talk', which enhances children's learning and understanding of mathematical ideas. Activities to do and questions to ask around the house and outside were given.

Chapter 4 provided five sets of problems for you to do with your children. They are arranged in order of increasing challenge. Very detailed explanations of how to solve them and solutions were also given.

We hope you enjoy mathematical problem solving with your children.

Bibliography

Cockcroft, W.H. (1982) *Mathematics Counts. Report of the Committee of Inquiry into the Teaching of Mathematics in Schools.* London: HMSO.

DES (1991) *Mathematics in the National Curriculum.* London: HMSO.

DfE (2013) *Mathematics programmes of study: Key stages 1 and 2. National Curriculum in England.* London:DfE.

DfEE (1999) *The Framework for Teaching Mathematics.* London: Department for Education and Employment.

HMI (Her Majesty's Inspectorate) (1985) *Mathematics 5-16: Curriculum Matters 3.* London: HMSO.

Koshy, V. (2017) *Teaching number with understanding: A handbook for primary school teachers.* Enrich Children's Lives. Middlesex.

National Curriculum Council (1992) *Using and Applying Mathematics Book* B. York: NCC.

Tough, P (2013) *How Children Succeed: Grit, Curiosity and the Hidden Power of Character.* London: Random House.

Printed in Great Britain
by Amazon

64618776R00047

GW00375005

SOMETHIN' ELSE

50S LIFE AND STYLE

SOMETHIN'ELSE
50s Life and Style

RUDOLPH **KENNA** WILLIAM **GRANDISON**

Richard Drew Publishing
GLASGOW

First published 1989 by
Richard Drew Publishing Limited
6 Clairmont Gardens, Glasgow G3 7LW
Scotland

Text © Rudolph Kenna 1989
Artwork © William Grandison 1989

British Library Cataloguing in Publication Data
Kenna, Rudolph
Somethin' else: 50s and style.
 1. Scotland. Social life, 1950-1959
 I. Title II. Grandison, William
 941.1'085'5

ISBN 0-86267-236-8

All rights reserved. No part of this publication
may be reproduced, stored in a retrieval system, or
transmitted, in any form or by any means, electronic,
mechanical, photocopying, recording or otherwise,
without the prior permission of the publisher.

Designed by William Grandison

Typeset by Swains (Glasgow) Limited

Printed and bound in Great Britain by Butler & Tanner
Frome and London

co ntents

intro

The 1950s were the American Years, when the war-supercharged energies of the world's richest and most powerful nation transformed the lives of millions of Americans and exerted a persuasive and lasting influence on the other peoples of the 'free world'. The USA was the land of the first consumer revolution, where cars sported wide chromium grins and housewives possessed 'dream kitchens'. The American mass-consumerist economy of the fifties duly became the model for similar developments worldwide.

As American 'mass-culture' took the Western world by storm, traditional attitudes and habits were subjected to change. The influence of the wealthy, status-conscious and super-confident America of the fifties can still be seen and felt worldwide. Jeans and T-shirts, aviator sunglasses and bikinis, barbecues and Coca-Cola, TV commercials and credit cards, supermarkets and parking meters, rock 'n' roll and transistor radios, all testify to the impact of the world's first full-blown consumer culture.

1

SOMETHIN' ELSE

Transatlantic Influences

Wealthy, super-con-
fident and immensely innovative, the USA
was at its peak of influence in the fifties.
Other Western democracies quickly
caught up in the prosperity stakes and
took to electric blankets, washing machines and refrigerators. But it was a long
time before remote-control TV eventually
conquered the world!

THE CADILLAC

Ne plus ultra of conspicuous consumption, it came from the same General Motors' stable as the affordable Chevy.

Transatlantic Influences

Coca-Cola's famous bottle was America's international style ambassador.

American living standards of the 1950s set a precedent for other advanced Western countries, and ultimately for the rest of the non-Communist world. In the early

The hula-hoop craze created a market for 60 million plastic rings by the end of the decade. The trick was keeping the hoop in motion by moving the pelvis like a Hawaiian hula dancer!

years of the decade, British newspapers and magazines frequently compared the lifestyles of similar groups of skilled workers in the USA and Great Britain, and usually concluded that the Americans were much better off, owning their own homes, cars and 'labour-

The *Ox in Flames* was Britain's first American-style, self-service drive-in restaurant. For one day only, girl 'car-hops' demonstrated outmoded drive-in practices.

Diners like this one in New York were an American institution, soon imitated in other countries.

saving' gadgets, while their British counterparts appeared to be working just as hard for the bare necessities of existence.

The United States pioneered 'planned obsolescence', which generated huge wealth for the economy. The spearhead of 'planned

obsolescence' was the automobile industry. In 1949 Harvey J. Earl of General Motors' styling department transposed the Lockheed Lightning tail-fin to the Cadillac range of cars. Earl's 'Motorama', a travelling circus of auto design, unveiled prototype 'dream cars' to the accompaniment of inimitable American razzmatazz, and the most popular styling gimmicks eventually reached the production

Personal juke boxes were a feature of diner counters.

In the late-fifties the British mass-circulation magazine *Picture Post* featured American movie stars such as Kim Novak, Marlon Brando and Grace Kelly.

American swooner crooners Johnny Ray and Frank Sinatra entertained wildly appreciative British audiences.

line. Earl's first post-war 'dream car' was the Buick Le Sabre (1954), inspired by the F-86 Sabre jet fighter.

The fabulous 'finned monsters', perfect expressions of 'rapid mobility and conspicuous expenditure', were uniquely representative of 1950s American consumerism at its most blatant. In 1957, when the Soviet Union provoked the USA into a 'space race' by launching Sputnik 1 (Bob Hope quipped: 'Their Germans are better than our Germans'), it was reported that many American car buyers, shocked and dismayed by their country's loss of prestige, 'went off' tail-fins and other aerospace gimmicks. While 'dream cars' and other 'excesses' of the American mass-market were denounced in no

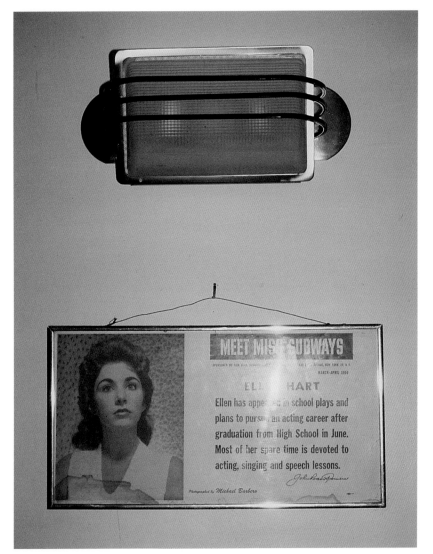

New York's famous 'Miss Subways' was immortalised in one of Hollywood's bounciest musicals — *On the Town*, starring Gene Kelly and Frank Sinatra.

uncertain terms by partisans of 'pure' form, other commentators were more indulgent. It was 'clearly absurd to demand that objects designed for a short useful life should exhibit qualities signifying eternal validity,' wrote Reyner Banham in 1955 in an influential essay entitled 'A Throw-Away Economy'.

Television was the first product of the 'new consumerism' to have a decisive influence on British social attitudes. A million new TV sets were purchased in the run-up to the Coronation in 1953. Since no one at that time regarded a television set as one of the 'bare necessities', this was a step in the direction of American-style living as seen in the movies. Cars provided another indicator to changing attitudes and

In 1956 Presleymania reached its height. *Love Me Tender*, Elvis Presley's first movie, played to packed houses.

PRESLEY

...SINGIN' MAN

...FIGHTIN' MAN

...LOVIN' MAN

A 20th CENTURY-FOX
CINEMASCOPE
PICTURE

E ME
DER 'U'

values. By 1959, one in three British families owned a car, compared with one in seven when the decade began. Hollywood movies and American TV sitcoms made the 'American way of life' appear immensely attractive. Americans were seen emerging from shiny cars, reclining in handsomely furnished 'split-level' living rooms, making calls on *bedroom* telephones, extracting goodies from huge refrigerators, and socialising at backyard barbecues. Few people in Britain were naïve enough to believe that Hollywood's larger-than-life Americans were typical of the population as a whole, but it was obvious that even many 'ordinary' Americans were enjoying an enviable lifestyle.

By the late-fifties, nearly four million women in Britain were going out to work, bringing home a second income and raising family living standards. The new priorities were 'consumer durables' such as refrigerators, toasters, pressure-cookers and irons. In the early years of the decade, kitchen appliances such as food-mixers had resembled industrial catering equipment of the same date, but product designers soon realised that forms reminiscent of factory and office equipment were a bad marketing device, destroying the illusion that

Fifties' America pioneered remote-controlled, portable and colour television. During the decade the number of TV sets owned by Americans rose from three million to fifty million.

the kitchen was a fun place, where 'labour-saving' appliances did all the work while the housewife stood around looking pretty in a frock that didn't clash with the washable wallpaper.

Many consumer products now taken for granted worldwide first appeared in the wealthy, technically advanced and status-conscious America of the fifties. Zenith remote-control TV featured 'flash-matic tuning' by means of 'a beam of magic light' that was 'absolutely harmless to humans'. RCA Victor's 'smartest, smallest Personal TV' was only $8\frac{1}{2}$ in. high, $9\frac{1}{2}$ in. wide and $12\frac{7}{8}$ in. long. General Electric blankets adjusted to temperature changes automatically and came in six colours. The Admiral clock-radio ('The clock-radio you don't plug in') had eight transistors and a battery life of 1000 hours. Unlike the showy, chromed and tail-finned 'dream car' — quintessentially American, and too esoteric to be widely assimilated abroad — the American 'dream-kitchen' became an almost universal status symbol, and by the end of the decade, in glossy magazines published in London, Paris and Rome, stylishly and impractically dressed women were depicted in settings of gleaming 'Sheer Line' kitchen appliances.

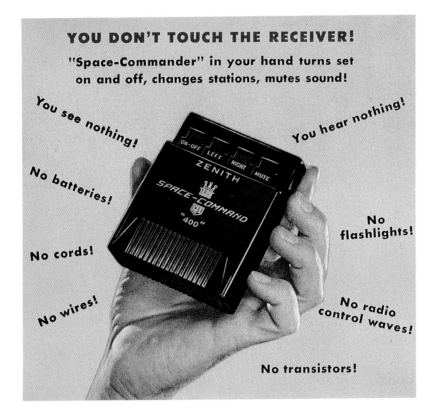

YOU DON'T TOUCH THE RECEIVER!

"Space-Commander" in your hand turns set on and off, changes stations, mutes sound!

You see nothing!

You hear nothing!

No batteries!

No flashlights!

No cords!

No wires!

No radio control waves!

No transistors!

The 'Space Commander' remote control TV tuner (1956) turned sets on and off, changed channels, muted sound, and eliminated long annoying commercials.

As American mass-culture successfully invaded Europe, anti-American feeling surfaced and was expressed in a variety of ways. Among the older generation of Britons, the feeling arose in part from the conviction that the Americans should have been 'on our side' in the Second World War right from the start, like 'the other English-speaking peoples'. Influential critics condemned the 'Coca-Colanisation' of Europe, and schoolteachers confiscated bubble gum and American comics. There was a mixed reaction to American living standards based on consumer credit. In pre-war Britain, hire-purchase had carried a social stigma, and even in the early-fifties many Britons felt that there was something indecent about prosperity on the 'never-never'. Television was instrumental in break-

Through TV, American celebrities like zany comedienne Lucille Ball achieved popularity on both sides of the Atlantic.

ing down the last bastions of resistance to hire-purchase. As soon as TV sets became readily available, almost everybody wanted them, even if they couldn't afford to pay cash. A 1956 survey showed that half the TVs in Britain had been purchased on HP. By 1958, although hire-purchase sales in Britain still only represented £10 per head of population against £70 a head in the USA, consumer credit had become respectable, and hire-purchase would soon be described as 'Britain's second banking system'.

In the USA, credit was by then a way of life. Never in American history had so many owed so much to so few. American consumer credit extended from the cradle to the grave. People were even buried

One of the most popular American TV sitcoms imported into Britain was *The Phil Silvers Show.*

R. J. Reynolds Tobacco Company, Winston-Salem, N. C.

See why Camel's the best-liked cigarette today!

Try a pack — or get yourself a carton. You'll really enjoy Camel's good,
rich taste and smooth mildness. And you'll see why more people
stay with Camels—year after year—than any other cigarette of any kind.

Only **CAMELS**

<u>taste</u> so rich~yet smoke so <u>mild</u>!

or cremated on the instalment plan. In 1960, with the 'market potential' of American teenagers estimated at around 10 million dollars a year, the merchandising director of *Seventeen* magazine advised US shopkeepers to 'start the credit habit in your store with your young customers'. Americans could buy almost *anything* on credit, from atomic shelters to African safaris. In the USA credit cards had become a sign of success, and a good credit rating was fast replacing church-going as the criterion of respectability. One notable advantage of the American attitude to credit was that manufacturers didn't have to cut corners in the specifications of their products. For Americans, the actual price of a refrigerator or washer was less important than looks and performance.

It was in the manufacturing field that the Americans exerted their most powerful and challenging influence. Between 1952 and 1962, American investment in Britain nearly trebled. By the end of 1960,

American singing cowboy movie star Roy Rogers, with his horse Trigger, had his own TV show in the fifties — spinning off a wide range of gifts, including 'Double-R-Bar' Brand boots and a genuine felt hat with adjustable chin-cord.

Walt Disney's Davy Crockett movies launched a new cult in the USA and Britain. Merchandisers were hard pressed to meet the demand for toys and accessories.

The American housewife was urged to 'feel like a queen' in her kitchen with an automatic dishwasher such as the Frigidaire, which could clean up to 147 pieces of glass and crockery at a time.

General Electric blankets had individual bedside controls, automatically adjusted to overnight temperature changes, and came in six high-fashion colours.

according to the US Department of Commerce, it had climbed to around £1,110,000,000. American investment was directed towards the new consumer and leisure industries at the expense of traditional industries such as shipbuilding. Names such as Westclox, Maxwell House, Kraft, Avon, Kellogg, Hoover and Bendix became household words in Britain as well as in the USA. By the end of the fifties, half the cosmetics, two-thirds of the foundation garments, three-quarters of the processed cheese products, two out of every three cars, and nine out of every ten razor blades sold in Britain were supplied by American-owned firms.

Britain's 'white-collar' workers drove to their offices on Good Year tyres, topping up with Esso petrol *en route*. At work, they used calculating machines and other equipment supplied by Remington-Rand and IBM. More than half the typewriters used in British offices were made in American-controlled factories. British men shaved with Gillette razor blades. British women wore Max Factor cosmetics. British children chewed Wrigley's Spearmint gum and consumed Spangles and Mars bars. Bird's custard, Carnation milk, Palmolive soap, Quaker breakfast cereals, Scotch tape, Tide and Daz soap powders — by the end of the decade the 'American connection' was formidable.

When Britain's first register of management consultants was compiled in the late 1940s, the total number of people engaged in the

Hamilton electric watches were described as 'the first basic improvement in 477 years of watchmaking history'.

profession was under three hundred. By the end of the fifties, the number of 'men in grey flannel suits' had increased to 1300, and there were twenty-eight firms engaged in the business, several with strong American affiliations.

Commercial TV came to Britain after a campaign masterminded by American advertising agencies. Britain's first commercial TV station,

Associated Rediffusion, began transmitting on 22 September 1955 at 7.15 p.m. To coincide with the inaugural ceremony, which was being televised from the Guildhall in London, wily BBC chiefs incinerated Grace Archer, star of their most popular radio soap opera. Almost eight million people tuned in to BBC Radio for the ritual sacrifice,

The deep-freezer — installed in the garage and filled directly from the car — offered the ultimate in one-stop grocery shopping.

SUPER-MARK

LETTUCE 2 for 35¢

LOCAL FRYERS ~ lb. 63¢

LARGE GRADE A EGGS 69¢ doz.

GRADE A BUTTER lb. 83¢

"You go ahead in. . . . I want to have a last few moments alone with my paycheck."

THE SATURDAY EVENING POST

An increasing proportion of family budgets went on pre-packed convenience foods. By the mid-fifties most American supermarkets were laid out in a carefully calculated manner, with 'impulse' items placed where they were sure to be noticed.

designed to take the wind out of Independent Television's sails. The nation's first 'commercial break' was presented by advertising agents Young & Rubicam on behalf of a popular brand of toothpaste ('It's tingling fresh . . . it's fresh as ice . . . it's Gibbs' toothpaste!'). Significantly, the other twenty-three commercials seen that historic night included plugs for American-owned companies such as Ford, Kraft, Esso and Remington-Rand. Since initially only 188,000 people in Britain had TVs capable of receiving the new commercial channel, there was little chance that the supermarkets would be inundated next day with customers.

Soon Britons were familiar with catchy TV jingles such as 'You'll wonder where the yellow went/When you brush your teeth with Pepsodent'. The proliferation of American-style advertising methods was not surprising, since some of the biggest advertising agencies in Britain were by now in American hands. By 1960, according to the *Financial Times*, four of the 'big ten' agencies in Britain were American-controlled. Britain's first American-style TV cash quiz show, *Double Your Money*, began on the commercial channel in

The backyard barbecue, a ritual of communal life in fifties' American suburbia, was soon to become popular worldwide.

September 1955. The first British TV quiz show, *What's My Line*, launched by the BBC in 1951 with Eamonn Andrews in the chair, originated as a CBS series in the USA in 1950. Associated Rediffusion's *Take Your Pick*, also seen for the first time in September 1955, celebrated the new consumerist ethos with 'star prizes', such as refrigerators and TV sets.

In the late-fifties, innate British conservatism appeared to be fighting a last-ditch battle against American-style mass-consumerism. But although Harold Macmillan, the Prime Minister, claimed that the British people had 'never had it so good', it was clear that, by American standards, Britain's consumer society had scarcely got off the launching pad. Ironically, the European nations which lost the Second World War — Germany and Italy — proved more receptive to the American message. Germany's *Wirtschaftswunder* and Italy's *Ricostruizione* were largely the outcome of the urgent need to sweep away all vestiges of the Nazi and Fascist past. The USA, where 'tomorrow's dreams come true today', was seen as the only possible model.

Originally a games room, and often located in the basement, the family room in the American suburban home frequently replaced the actual living room as the focus of family life.

2

SOMETHIN' ELSE

Forms 'n' Fashions

The inventive fifties embraced the rigid geometry of Le Corbusier as well as the extremes of sci-fi. Paris dominated the world of *haute couture* with Rue de la Paix — inspired elegance, but Teddy boys and beatniks opened the door to a wider interpretation of style.

THE HAWAIIAN SHIRT

Swaying hula dancers under a tropical moon, ukelele music, and surf riding on the gentle rollers of Waikiki beach were among the attractions which brought Americans to Honolulu and helped make Hawaii's colourful Aloha shirts fashionable. Bermuda shorts were another vacation-inspired fifties' fashion craze.

Forms 'n' Fashions

Some of the coolest shades of the fifties carried the Ray Ban trademark.

The **1950s was the jet decade,** when the sound barrier fell to aviation technology. Product design absorbed images and symbolism derived from jet flight. One Pifco hairdryer resembled the nacelle of a jet aircraft, and even oven glass was named Jetware. Radios, cookers and car dashboards had dials reminiscent of aircraft control panels.

In the early-fifties, 'streamlined' shapes could still be seen every-where, though 'streamlining' itself was largely outmoded. It had first been applied to locomotives, aeroplanes and automobiles, and by

See how Ray-Ban® G-15 Sun Glasses open your eyes to safer driving!

Sunglasses and eyeglasses, like cars, expressed their owners' personalities and were made of coloured plastics, sometimes wingshaped and sprayed with glitter dust or inlaid with semi-precious stones.

the early-forties it had come to symbolise efficiency. Hundreds of manufacturers accordingly leaped onto the bandwagon, applying the technique indiscriminately to refrigerators, cookers, radios, and many other products that were obviously not going anywhere in a hurry. By the Jet-Age fifties, the bulbous curves of 'streamlined moderne' no longer evoked associations of record-breaking cars and planes, and when Oldsmobile used rocket imagery in advertisements for their 'streamlined' cars, they succeeded in being amusing instead of convincing. 'Streamlining' was now seen as a stylistic aberration, little better than the zigzags and chevrons of 'jazz modern', as art deco was then called, and designers of the fifties universally abandoned it in favour of 'sensible' boxy shapes such as those which were being popularised by contemporary architects.

The fifties saw the triumph of the Modern Movement in architecture, with traditional building styles almost entirely superseded. 'Style', in fact, became a term of abuse, for the word implied impermanence, and the great 'truths' of the Modern Movement were obviously 'eternal' ones. Avant-garde architects of the thirties, in-

Shades were
important
fashion
accessories -
adding finishing
touches to
stylish outfits.

By the mid-fifties hairdressing had become a boom industry. The Immensely popular 'Tony Curtis' hairstyle featured a heavily greased forward-set wave, swept back behind the ears into a point at the back of the head.

Girl wearing skirt
decorated with rock 'n'
roll motifs.

cluding Le Corbusier and Mies van der Rohe had become, by the fifties, the idols and mentors of a new generation of architects, busy creating an environment of office blocks, shopping precincts and housing estates. Few paused to reflect that the victory of the Modern Movement, a minority movement before the Second World War, had not been quite as 'inevitable' as its supporters maintained. It owed its extraordinary success to a number of factors, not least of which was the war itself.

After the Second World War, impoverished and bomb-scarred European nations had to rebuild quickly, and expensive, labour-intensive and time-consuming traditional building techniques were simply out of the question. Post-war social idealism was another significant factor. In Britain, the wartime Coalition Government had promised everyone a better life 'after the war' and had backed up their promises with extremely effective propaganda, such as Abram Games's famous poster of 1942 depicting a new, glass-walled school with the slogan 'Your Britain — Fight For It Now'.

Savile Row's 'Edwardian Look' inspired the Teddy boy's draped jacket with velvet trim. Teddy girls wore flouncy dirndl skirts with paper nylon petticoats and flat shoes suitable for energetic dancing.

It seemed that the time had come to build a new society with new techniques and materials and, most importantly, with a new aesthetic. The latter was provided by the 'functional tradition' as championed by Nikolaus Pevsner, Henry-Russell Hitchcock and other highly influential writers. Young architects of the fifties looked to Weimar Germany's Bauhaus for inspiration — and fortunately the pre-war Bauhaus was untainted by Nazism. The future course of post-war architecture might have been very different if the Nazis hadn't closed the Bauhaus and announced their opposition to 'machines for living in'.

The widespread influence of the Bauhaus over 1950s American architects has since been wittily described in Tom Wolfe's book *From Bauhaus to Our House*. Ironically, it was the 'corporate office style' of American 'big business' which most closely reflected Bauhaus

'Miracle' synthetic fabrics such as Dacron (Terylene), Acrilan and Orlon meant wash 'n' wear clothes that were crisp, cool, and seldom needed ironing.

precepts. But Bauhaus influence was not confined to architecture. Many craft designers, including weavers, potters and woodworkers, disturbed by the 'corrupt' values and rampant materialism of the consumer society, tried to dedicate their lives, in the words of the potter Marguerite Wildenhain, 'to an idea that is not based on success and money, but on human independence and dignity'.

One result of the 1950s infatuation with 'the world of tomorrow' was an interest in interplanetary travel that was wildly disproportionate to the state of the art — the first earth satellite, the Soviet Union's Sputnik, didn't hit the headlines until October 1957. Flying saucers were sighted in many parts of the world, though for some inexplicable reason most of the sightings were in the USA. The science-fiction boom of the fifties kept flying saucers and other UFOs newsworthy throughout the decade. Magazines ran features and serials on the theme of space travel, postulating such marvels as atomic-powered liners to Mars and Venus, and science-fiction movies played to packed houses. Ralph Tubbs's metal-clad Dome of Discovery at the Festival of Britain was like a gigantic, earth-moored flying saucer, an effect enhanced by night-time illumination. Little boys got spacemen outfits as Christmas presents, and sci-fi influences entered the home, with table lamps and room heaters that looked like everyone's idea of flying saucers. TVs, standing on splayed legs and sprouting antennas, were themselves 'one-eyed monsters' reminiscent of the menacing or comical aliens in the movies.

Throughout the fifties, atomic power held the threat of annihilation and the promise of energy harnessed for peaceful pur-

Before the late-fifties' 'youthquake' revolutionised young men's fashions, flamboyant ties were principal means of sartorial self-expression.

poses. With Three Mile Island and Chernobyl a generation ahead, there seemed no limit to the peaceful applications of atomic power. 'You and the Obedient Atom' was the snappy title of one magazine feature in which scientists predicted nuclear-powered ships and aircraft 'in the near future'. As the decade progressed, atomic imagery proliferated, and molecular models inspired designers worldwide.

The 1951 Festival of Britain unveiled the 'contemporary' style that soon became the dominant design idiom in Britain. The Festival Pattern Group produced designs based on crystalline formations and molecular structures, and one of the most interesting sights of the Festival, Edward Mills's giant 'Abacus' of plastic balls, was clearly inspired by atomic models. By the end of the decade, products such as

Toreador pants — tight,
just below knee-length
casuals — were in vogue
at Clayton High School,
St Louis.

TOREADOR**PANTS**

textiles and wallpapers had appeared with motifs borrowed from molecular structures.

George Nelson's famous ball clock, designed for the Herman Miller Clock Company, was one of the most successful 'molecular' designs of the fifties. Less attractive, but still interesting, were the TV ornaments which still turn up in junk shops and street markets. Designed to sit on top of the TV and show that their owners were attuned to the *Zeitgeist*, these were eye-shaped, contained mirrors or mounted butterflies, and incorporated 'molecular structure' motifs. The so-called 'cocktail cherry style' captured the innocent flavour of an era when magazine feature writers promised readers a bright Atomic Future of cheap and plentiful energy and assured them that atmospheric pollution would soon be a thing of the past. The most famous 'cocktail cherry' atomic model of the fifties was the Atomium at the 1958 Expo Fair in Brussels. Its nine spheres were covered in

Swimsuit by Rose Marie Reid. modelled in a setting inspired by Botticelli's *Birth of Venus* (1959).

Sportswear in new lightweight, crease-resistant fabrics — increasingly seen on the beach and on board ship.

British pop singer Marty Wilde and his bride Joyce, honeymooning in the USA, sport typical fifties' swimwear fashions.

shiny aluminium foil, and viewing platforms were located in the central and topmost spheres.

Amoeba-like 'free forms' of the fifties provided a welcome respite from the severe geometry of Bauhaus-inspired architects and designers. 'Free form' furniture was pioneered by Isamu Noguchi,

W·S·GRANDISON

Vladimir Kagan and other avant-garde designers, and by the end of the decade makers of mass-produced furniture were turning out millions of coffee tables in the shape of kidneys and boomerangs.

Pablo Picasso, Paul Klee and Joan Miró were among the famous modern artists who influenced the appearance and decoration of ordinary mass-produced objects in the fifties. By a strange paradox, their influence was sometimes most evident in kitsch, such as cheap pottery, the shapes and decoration of which were 'modern' in a loud and incoherent fashion. Mass-produced ceramic lamp bases incised

Collarless, semi-fitted jackets and capes were worn with pencil-slim skirts, slit for ease of movement. Elbow-length gloves were *de rigueur* with stylish day and cocktail outfits.

With the introduction of shorter hairstyles, make-up increasingly emphasized the eyes. The 'doe-eyed' look of mascara-outlined eyes with slightly elongated corners was accentuated by thickly pencilled eyebrows. The long slender necks of the fifties were enhanced with chiffon scarves or glamorous jewellery inspired by nostalgia for the Roaring Twenties.

with 'artistic' graffiti are now among the least-coveted artefacts of the fifties. Yet at the time, their proud owners doubtlessly valued them way above the Negro heads, toreadors and ballerinas of their less sophisticated neighbours.

The most potent American symbol of the fifties was the 'dream car', chromed from end to end, with upswept tail-fins and V-arched tail-lights, its sleek, low-slung lines enhanced by white sidewalls and two-tone paintwork. The essence of the 'dream car' was 'the one hundred million dollar look', whether the car was an up-market Cadillac, a middle-range Oldsmobile, or a low-priced Chevrolet. Americans were promised 'tomorrow's cars today' and 'cars that turn heads as *no* cars did before'. Car stylists, advertising copywriters and graphic designers combined to make the American dream come true, and looked to the jet aircraft for inspiration. The new fuel-hungry and space-consuming breed of autos had flight-sweep styling, strato-streak engines, jet-flo bumpers, and touch-down overdrive, and were engineered to 'break through the vibration barrier'. The space-age car seemed to be just around the next corner. General Motors' Firebird II, an experimental prototype described as 'America's first touring turbine car', was the star attraction at the 1957 London Motor Show. The body of the futuristic monster was made of expensive titanium, and steering was by crossbar.

New idea in plastics...

improves everything from golf clubs to TV cabinets!

Plastics came of age in the consumerist fifties and were used for everything from Tupperware food containers to hair lacquers. Trade names such as Polythene and Cellophane became household words.

Cocktail bars and diners were decorated with laminated plastics such as Warerite and Formica.

The Skylon and Dome of Discovery, features of the 1951 Festival of Britain, were among the influential sci-fi shapes of the fifties.

In the early-fifties, when the Chrysler Corporation assumed rashly that Americans bought cars on an entirely rational basis and started to market compact autos without frills, the company's share of the market plummeted by around 13 per cent. Chrysler then began to produce long, low cars and, by selling dreams, soon regained a substantial share of the market. The motivational researchers discovered that though men bought practical four-door sedans and married sensible girls who could cook, they hankered after glitzy convertibles and alluring *femmes fatales*. Dealers found that the best

Symbolising the peaceful uses of the atom and covered in shiny aluminium foil, the Atomium, centrepiece of Expo 58 in Brussels, represented an enormously magnified metallic crystal.

Frank Lloyd Wright's Guggenheim Museum in New York and Oscar Niemeyer's superb buildings in Brasilia were among the most influential architectural achievements of the fifties.

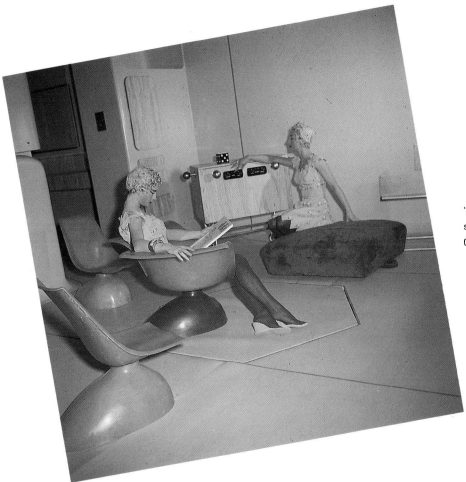

'Home of the Future' on
show at London's
Olympia, 1956.

way to draw more males into their showrooms was to display
convertibles in their windows. The hardtop, described by a leading
psychologist as a symbolic union of wife (sedan) and mistress
(convertible), was introduced and duly became the most successful
new auto to appear in America for years.

According to a study made for the *Chicago Tribune* by Social
Research Inc, Cadillac owners were 'middle-aged' and 'responsible';
Ford owners were 'upper lower class' and 'practical'; De Soto owners
were 'upper middle class' and 'proud'; Studebaker owners were
'sophisticated' and 'intellectual'; and Pontiac owners were 'middle of
the road' and 'conventional'. In American magazine advertisements
of the period, Cadillac owners were shown emerging from exclusive
hotels and prestigious museums and art galleries. Ford owners were

usually about to set out on family picnics. If the advertisements were anything to go by, Chevrolet owners had more fun than all the rest put together.

Where automobiles were concerned, safety was gradually becoming a major sales factor. Nylon and rayon cord offered greater

Vacuum cleaners, and even TV antennas, reflected the decade's sci-fi enthusiasms. The Hoover Constellation 'walked on air' and could almost 'read your mind', following you around the house like an indulgent extra-terrestrial.

protection against tyre failure on the new superhighways. Other safety measures included steering wheels with recessed centres, padded instrument panels, and seat belts, said to be 'one-third stronger than required for airlines'. By 1962, when Ralph Nader's famous book *Unsafe At Any Speed* was first published, the finned

As the space age approached, futurist fantasies proliferated. The American family looked forward to midwinter sunbathing and driving a car straight out of a sci-fi movie.

Be sure with PURE

monsters — triumphs of 'built-in obsolescence' — were already heading for the scrapyard in fulfilment of their destiny.

Chemistry and mass-production together revolutionised leisure wear in the 1950s. Polyester and acrylic fibres meant lightweight, easy-care clothing that stayed neat through repeated wearing and seldom needed ironing. Skirts were permanently pleated, and shirts and blouses could be hung up to 'drip-dry'. The United States led the world in casual wear. Colourful and informal clothes were doubly welcome after the drab uniformity of the war years. The choice ranged from sports jackets and slacks to Hawaiian shirts and Bermuda shorts. Some casual fashions were directly inspired by Hollywood. Walt Disney's Davy Crockett movies created a short-lived vogue for moccasins and fringed jackets, while *Shane* (1953)

In fifties' America, more people drove Chevrolets than any other make of car. The 1957 Bel Air range was described as 'sweet, smooth and sassy'.

The 1955 De Soto
Sportsman featured
fashionable two-tone
bodywork and white-wall
tyres.

helped to popularise the working clothes of the American cowboy.
Lumberjack plaids became fashionable, and a hundred years after
Levi Strauss manufactured the original Levi's for the gold-rush
miners of California, blue denim jeans became popular with both
sexes.

In 1953 *Vogue* advised readers to buy sweaters 'two sizes larger for
a casual look', but many women preferred to wear figure-hugging
sweaters and skirts in emulation of 'screen goddesses' Jane Russell,
Jayne Mansfield and Marilyn Monroe. Busts, like American cars,
embodied the 'forward look' and the sweater-girl bra, containing
stiffened cones, pushed breasts upwards and outwards. Padded foam
rubber 'falsies' also helped women to improve on nature and culti-
vate what the French called 'le busty-look americaine'.

Sporty clothes were no longer exclusive to tennis players, golfers
or yachtsmen, but were being worn on informal occasions by almost
everyone. Long or short-sleeved sports shirts and T-shirts in bright
colours and lightweight crease-resistant synthetics were sold by the

American cars of the fifties wore chrome jewellery with panache. Horizontal grilles made cars appear lower and wider.

million. The Hawaiian shirt was by far the most colourful casual garment of the period. The early shirts were works of applied art, screen-printed on raw silk or quality rayon, but by the fifties mass-production was in full swing, and the shirts were being machine-printed in huge quantities. Women's sportswear occasionally struck a high-fashion note and included jumpers, tailored slacks, play-

"Yes, you can make it."

THE SATURDAY EVENING POST

suits and shorts. Scanty two-piece swimsuits called 'bikinis', named after the atomic bomb test at Bikini Atoll, were at the height of their popularity in the fifties, but one-piece swimwear remained fashionable and was frequently produced in exotic designs. By the late-fifties, Italian designers such as Simonetta and Pucci were producing elegant and sophisticated casual clothes that could be worn on more formal occasions than backyard barbecues.

The 'Italian Look' was part of an Italian vogue at that time which included espresso bars, pop songs such as 'Volare' and 'Arrivedérci, Roma', movies starring Gina Lollobrigida and Sophia Loren, Vespa and Lambretta motor-scooters, and stiletto heels. Italian casual clothes and sportswear were chic, and were produced in very bright colours. By the end of the decade the 'Look' had been taken up by British working-class youths, who wore Italian-style suits.

Sportswear and casualwear were incomplete without sunglasses.

Annual style changes quickly dated American cars, propelling consumers towards the ultimate goal of a fashionable new model every year.

The most freaky shades of the fifties — striped or mottled in bright colours — produced an upswept, cat's-eye effect, reminiscent of the eye masks worn by Mardi Gras revellers. Fluorescent socks, pullovers

Swept-wing jet airplanes were a major source of inspiration for American car stylists 'Flight Sweep' styling was a feature of 1957 Fireflite sedans, hardtops and convertibles, from the De Soto Division of Chrysler Corporation.

This baby can flick its tail at anything on the road!

SWEPT·WING
'57 *Dodge*

and slacks were popular with teenagers, especially rock 'n' rollers. The jazz revival, a musical phenomenon of the fifties, fostered hundreds of clubs and bands, and also influenced fashions. Jazz trends were towards beards, rolled jeans, jangly ear-rings and urchin cuts.

In the fifties Paris was basking in an Indian summer of *haute couture*, with Christian Dior, Gabrielle 'Coco' Chanel, Cristobal Balenciaga and Jacques Fath among the supreme arbiters of style. While the high priests of *couture* set the fashions, the mass market spread their pronouncements worldwide. By the middle of the decade, chainstores in the USA and Europe were offering inexpensive clothes modelled on exclusive Paris fashion lines. British *couturier* Hardy Amies opened a boutique in London's Savile Row as early as 1950, selling stylish ready-to-wear clothes, and in 1955 Mary Quant followed suit with her boutique, Bazaar, in King's Road, Chelsea, forerunner of hundreds of trendy boutiques in the swinging London

Early-fifties rocket imagery was brought into play to help sell conventionally streamlined Oldsmobile cars.

of the sixties.

Dior's revolutionary and ultra-feminine 'New Look' of 1947 had highlighted women's waists and hips. Skirts were either very narrow and tapered or very full and flared. The most popular full skirt was the dirndl style. The figure-hugging clothes of the fifties led to a boom in foundation garments, including shaped bras, elastic pantie girdles, and boned corselettes called 'waspies'. In that pre-ecology era, fur coats and stoles were objects of almost universal admiration, and mink was the ultimate in sartorial status symbols.

Paris was influential in the fifties in other respects besides *haute couture*. 'Gay Paree', unscathed by wartime bombing, had opened its doors to another generation of tourists, many of whom were abroad for the first time. Less prosperous — but also less supercilious — than the pampered patricians of the *belle époque*, their enthusiasm was contagious and was captured in movies such as *Innocents in Paris* and *An American in Paris*. Headscarves and china plates were decorated with Parisian motifs. Ornaments, jewellery and coffee tables assumed artists' palette shapes. Models were photographed against a backdrop of the Palais de Chaillot or the Place Vendôme. French poodles became fashion accessories, and beatniks cultivated a picturesque, 'Left Bank' appearance. On a less frivolous level, intellectuals such as Jean-Paul Sartre and Simone de Beauvoir successfully upheld the French capital's reputation as a *ville lumier*.

More conservative than their American counterparts, and less subject to market pressures, British car designers sometimes achieved timeless *concour d'elegance* perfection of line, epitomised by the Jaguar XK 120 coupe.

Fifties' 'bubble' cars such as the BMW-Isetta two-seater were manufactured in Europe, Japan, South America, Australia and the USA. Wits called them 'Easter eggs on roller skates'!

3

SOMETHIN' ELSE

Consumer Revolution

ifties' USA provided the rest of the developed world with its model for a phenomenally successful consumer society. American movies and TV sitcoms gave other nations a foretaste of the promised land of mass-consumerism, where cars sporting wide chromium grins were renewed every two or three years, and every other housewife possessed a 'dream kitchen' full of nifty gadgets.

1951 MAJESTIC

In the early-fifties streamlining — the height of fashion ten years before — still influenced the shapes of refrigerators, cars and many other products. Radios like the Majestic had miniature valves. By the end of the decade transistors — pioneered in Bell Telephone Laboratories and installed in the first American satellites — made radios truly portable.

By the late-fifties, American-style consumerism had taken root in other Western countries. Housewives, abandoning the thrifty ways of their mothers and grandmothers, bought prepacked convenience foods. Advertising was increasingly directed towards the young married woman with her greater personal freedom, larger household budget, and natural desire to escape tedium and drudgery.

Consumer Revolution

Campbell's Vegetable Beef Soup!

Self-service supermarkets revolutionised shopping. Meat and vegetables were 'Cellophane-fresh'. Weights and prices were clearly indicated.

By the rest of the developed world's modest standards, American consumerism in the fifties was legendary. Visitors to the USA returned, Marco Polo-like, wide-eyed with tales of flavoured toothpaste, colour and remote-control TV, elevators with piped music, and cars equipped with tissue boxes and vanity cases. Outside the USA, millions dreamed of American 'egalitarian' affluence. When one British working-class family won a fortune on the football pools, their priorities significantly included a pink Chevrolet Impala and a holiday in Las Vegas.

Mass-consumerism came earlier in the USA than in other developed countries, pioneered by industrialists such as Henry Ford. By the early-fifties, Americans already had cars, washing machines, cookers and other 'consumer durables' in relative abundance. To

Widespread use of plastic bags proved hazardous to young children, a danger unwittingly prefigured in this naive advertisement for Du Pont Cellophane.

DU PONT Cellophane

Mom says
I'm so fresh
and so clean
(*sometimes*)—
she ought to
wrap me in
Cellophane
to keep me
that way.

keep the economy expanding (the spectre of the Great Depression still loomed large) they had to be convinced of the need to consume more and more. In the nick of time, social scientists and psychologists rescued America's captains of industry with startling insights into often irrational consumer behaviour.

By the mid-fifties motivation analysis was a multi-million dollar industry and merchandisers were learning to sell emotional security, ego gratification and sexual reassurance along with their products. American advertising executives pored over tomes such as Reik's *Masochism in Modern Man* and Pavlov's *Lectures on Conditioned Reflexes*. Big Madison Avenue agencies hired psychologists and sociologists to conduct studies exploring the consumer's subsurface desires, needs and drives, a process probed by Vance Packard in his critically perceptive bestseller *The Hidden Persuaders,* first published in 1957.

American expenditure on advertising rose from three billion

In the fifties no country in the world equalled the USA in the consumption of tobacco products. Three-quarters of American men and two-fifths of American women smoked.

"Won't anybody cigarette me?"

dollars in 1950 to nine billion dollars in 1955. Manufacturers took their cue from car makers — already adept at creating psychological obsolescence by means of annual changes in styles, colours and specifications. Merchandisers became symbol conscious, as motivational researchers solemnly drew their attention to the 'strong moral code' of the lower middle classes or the 'relaxed, carefree and uninhibited' behaviour of lower-bracket social groups.

In 1948, Lloyd Warner of the University of Chicago divided Americans into six social classes. His fourth and fifth classes — the 'lower middle' and 'upper lower' — constituted the Middle Majority, representing about 65 per cent of the population, a formidable concentration of the nation's purchasing power. With consumer research showing American women controlling up to 80 per cent of family purchasing decisions, Mrs Middle America became an image to conjure with, an advertising man's Helen of Troy, destined to launch innumerable campaigns and products.

The medical profession and sports personalities endorsed smoking, though scientists were already issuing warnings connecting cigarettes with heart disease and lung cancer, leading to a boom in filter tip sales such as the young and hip Hit Parade brand.

By the fifties the supermarket was an American institution.

The marketing revolution stimulated consumer demand, creating wants that people still weren't fully aware of. In a 1955 Ford advertisement, *two* cars were prescribed as a 'must' for the modern family, and 'Fords by the pair' was optimistically described as 'America's new buying habit'. American-Standard announced that 'a second bathroom is a must in most homes these days' and offered luxury-loving customers monogrammed faucets. On Mother's Day and Father's Day — synthetic consumerist holy days — sales of perfume, chocolates, socks and shaving cream soared in a gratifying manner recalling annual Christmas bonanzas.

With women playing a much greater part in determining American buying habits, products such as bourbon, beer and cars

assumed less macho images. Sometimes, however, the process was reversed. Filter-tipped Marlboro cigarettes changed their feminine brand image in response to cancer fears, and Marlboro advertisements began to feature cowboys, sailors and other he-men, all of whom sported a veteran's tattoo on the backs of their hands.

The United States had pioneered self-service markets in the twenties, and by the early-fifties the supermarket had become a national institution. Critics argued, however, that in the drive for efficiency, supermarket planners had gone too far. Packages were eye-catching, prices clearly marked, and meat and vegetables were sealed in hygienic Cellophane. But somehow the human element was neglected. By the mid-fifties, store-planners were collaborating with interior designers, putting glamour into the groceries by means of murals, special lighting effects, canned music and cheerful colour schemes.

Until 1948 there were no self-service stores in Britain. A decade later, there were 6000, including 250 supermarkets with American-style features such as coffee bars and background music. TV commercials — first seen in Britain in 1955 — helped to establish brand loyalties, popularising 'miracle ingredients' such as Gardol, GL-70 and Fluoristan.

"That's just one third down and 24 backbreaking payments."

THE SATURDAY EVENING POST

4

SOMETHIN' ELSE

Teens

Booming consumerist fifties' America gave rise to a new market force — the teenager, whose purchasing power, though limited, was untramelled by adult responsibilities. Teenagers spent a disproportionate amount of their earnings on leisure and entertainment, and by the end of the decade had come into their own kingdom of clothes, records and movies.

BUDDY HOLLY —

First-generation teen idol Buddy Holly's legacy of songs, including 'Peggy Sue', together with his death in a plane crash in 1959 aged only twenty-two, ensured his survival as a pop legend. He was one of the first rock musicians to popularise the electric guitar and his personal favourite was a $600 Fender Stratocaster.

Teens

Teenagers on Jones Beach, Long Island, New York.

The affluent, consumerist USA of the fifties gave rise to a new social class: teenagers. The term was unfamiliar at first, and 'teen-agers' were frequently encountered in newspapers and magazines, but by the end of the decade movies with titles such as *Teenage Rebel, Teenage Doll* and *Teenagers From Outer Space* showed that the new 'in-between' age group had won social acceptance, its likes and dislikes studied by advertisers and merchandisers, while teenage expressions such as 'with it' and

In the late-fifties American juke boxes were installed in many British cafes, coffee bars and clubs, proving immensely popular with teenagers, whose musical tastes were largely ignored by the media.

'Daddy-o' had achieved currency throughout the English-speaking world.

As early as 1945, Eugene Gilbert, an enterprising eighteen-year-old American, established an agency called Gil-Bert Teen Age Services to advise firms on ways to exploit the new eldorado, the 'in-between-age' market. According to Gilbert, marketing to teenagers was 'quite unlike marketing to any other portion of the total market'. New techniques were required, based on 'deep insight into their habits, ideas and thoughts'. By 1957 Gilbert's agency had become a multi-million-dollar concern. Plans to open a permanent London office fell through, however, for after coming to Britain to survey the situation, Gilbert concluded that the British youth market lacked the potential for significant growth.

Subsequent events proved him wrong, but the American and British teenage markets were certainly very different in a number of respects. In the USA, the youth market appeared to embrace all sections of the teenage population, while in Britain the market seems largely to have been working-class. British middle-class teenagers

Mass hysteria at rock 'n' roll concerts increasingly emphasized the 'generation gap' between teenagers and other age groups.

The Buddy Holly Story
THE SOUND OF
CORAL
HIGH-FIDELITY
LVA 9105

were apparently too busy investing in their future to throw themselves wholeheartedly into the new 'youth culture'.

Much of the teenage consumer spending in Britain at that time was
done by young working-class boys and girls with boring, 'dead-end'
jobs. With teenage earnings more than 50 per cent higher than before
the Second World War, they were able to express their individuality
through dress and leisure-time activities. Clothing manufacturers,
who had previously lumped adolescents and young adults along with
children, now sat up and took notice, and the British *Drapers' Record*
warned that 'the teenage trade cannot be treated as a sideline'.

The older generation
was scandalised by
teenage pop idols such
as Elvis Presley, whose
provocative stage act
earned him the
expressive sobriquet of
'the Pelvis'.

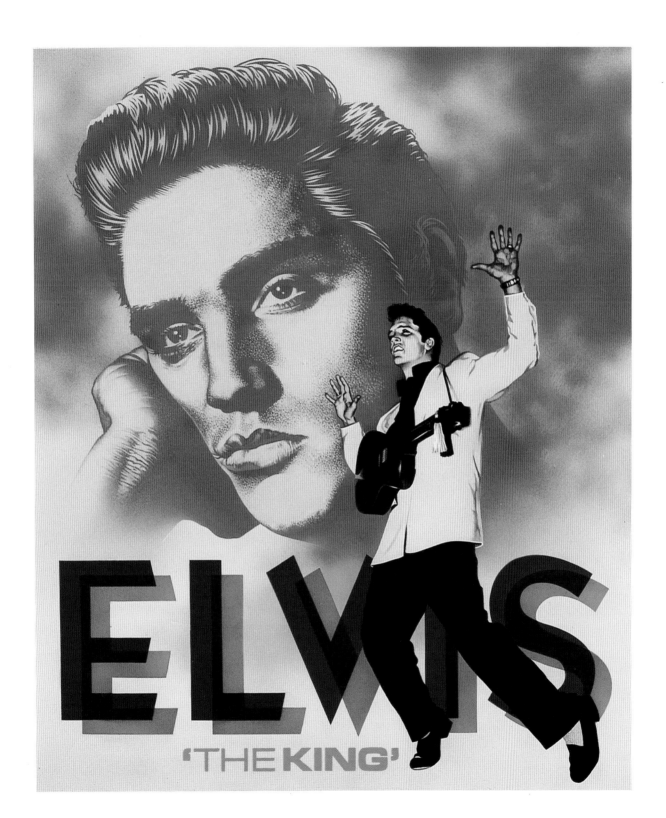

One of the major agents of teenage emancipation was the 45 rpm micro-groove plastic disc, pioneered in the USA. 'Rock Around the Clock', recorded in 1954, marked the beginning of teenage music, selling 15 million copies worldwide. Bill Haley, thirty years old, paunchy, and married with a family, was an unlikely teenage heart-throb, but with the arrival of Elvis Presley, Buddy Holly, Chuck Berry,

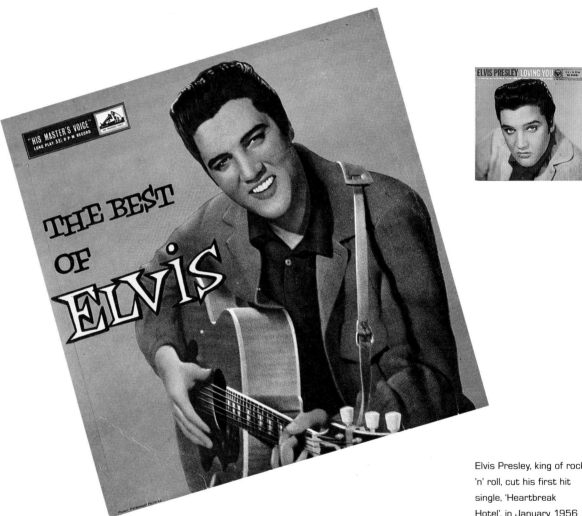

Elvis Presley, king of rock 'n' roll, cut his first hit single, 'Heartbreak Hotel', in January 1956 and sold millions of records in the first two years of his phenomenal career.

Little Richard and Eddie Cochran, rock 'n' roll became the perfect expression of teenage attitudes and aspirations.

At first, rock 'n' roll was entirely ignored by British radio and TV, which consistently featured 'ballad' singers such as Ruby Murray, Dickie Valentine, Rosemary Squires, Dennis Lotis, Joan Regan, and David Whitfield. The first teen-style pop music programme on

British TV was Associated Rediffusion's *Cool for Cats*. First seen in December 1956, it illustrated records with dancers and visuals such as multiple-picture effects. BBC followed commercial TV's lead in February 1957 with *6.5 Special*, introduced by Pete Murray and Josephine Douglas. BBC TV's *Juke Box Jury* began in July 1959. David Jacobs chaired the programme, which voted new records 'hits' or 'misses' and brought fame to new arrivals on the pop scene, such as Adam Faith and Billy Fury.

By the mid-fifties, Hollywood moguls had zoomed in on the

British teen idols of the fifties dressed less flamboyantly than their American counterparts, but Cliff Richard helped to popularise black shirts and white ties.

lucrative teen market. In *The Wild One* (1954) Marlon Brando led a motor-cycle gang called the Black Rebels; the movie was not shown commercially in Britain until 1968. *Rebel Without a Cause*, exploring juvenile delinquency in affluent middle-class America, was released in 1955. The following year saw the first-ever rock movie, *Rock Around the Clock*, starring Bill Haley and the Comets. Movies such as *Blackboard Jungle* and *High School Confidential* introduced a bemused older generation to teenage 'hep' jargon.

The film actor regarded as an *enfant terrible*, James Dean, died in a car crash on US Highway 466 in 1956, like 38,300 other Americans that year. Other teen idols, including Buddy Holly and Eddie Cochran, also died in tragic circumstances, and, by dying young, earned a special place in the rock pantheon of fame. Perhaps as a result of the untimely demise of real-life contemporary heroes such as Holly and Cochran, morbid teenage 'death songs' with titles such as 'Endless Sleep', 'Teen Angel', and 'Tell Laura I Love Her' became popular. Drowning in a swollen river or expiring in the mangled wreck of a crashed car, the victims remained teenagers forever.

Elvis Aron Presley, the most idolised of those teen idols who, in Thom Gunn's phrase, 'turned revolt into a style', died in 1977 aged

Jivin' at an evening dancing session in an English comprehensive school, 1957. By the late-fifties teenagers were clamouring for non-stop rock 'n' roll music.

In 1954 Bill Haley and the Comets recorded 'Rock Around the Clock'. Used as the opening music for MGM's *Blackboard Jungle*, it achieved cult status, and rock 'n' roll was born.

ROCK 'N' ROLL STAGE SHOW
BILL HALEY
and his comets

forty-two, having disappointed many early Presley worshippers by a lifestyle which grew increasingly bizarre as the years went by. Yet Presley's impact on the 'youth culture' of the late-fifties was unique. From 1956 onwards, he was the uncrowned king of rock 'n' roll, mentor of innumerable young hopefuls, including John Lennon and Elton John. Having made his first hit record, 'Heartbreak Hotel', in January of that year, he went on to sell millions of discs and, under the astute management of 'Colonel' Tom Parker, gross a hundred million dollars within the first two years of his rise to stardom.

Presley's early movies, *Love Me Tender* (1956), *Loving You* and *Jailhouse Rock* (1957), were among the first Hollywood musicals aimed at the teenage market. At the height of Presley-mania, teenagers all over the Western world wore Elvis Presley T-shirts, chewed Elvis Presley bubble gum, and wrote with Elvis Presley

Legendary American rock 'n' roller Eddie Cochran was only 21 when he died in a car crash near London airport in April 1960, at the end of a $2\frac{1}{2}$ month tour of Britain.

'King of skiffle' Lonnie Donegan and fans on *6.5 Special*, BBC TV's first teen show, launched in 1957. Donegan's LP was the first from Britain to feature in the American top thirty.

Adam Faith was one of the idols of Britain's first teenage generation.

ballpoint pens. Astute businessmen were quick to realise that the young generation wanted to look like their rock 'n' roll heroes. Merchandising spin-offs from the new pop culture included Elvis Presley posters, magazines, books, pictures and guitars. Thousands of fashion-conscious teenage boys in crowded dance halls must have echoed Presley's plaint: 'You can do anything but lay off of my blue suede shoes.'

In spite of explosive pseudonyms such as Marty Wilde and Billy Fury (not to mention Vince Eager and Duffy Power), Britain's home-grown rock 'n' roll performers seemed tame beside Elvis Presley, Little Richard, Jerry Lee Lewis, Gene Vincent, and other American stars. Early rock 'n' roll was, after all, indigenous to the USA, with roots in the music of American blacks. When Bill Haley fused the black American rhythm 'n' blues idiom with country-and-western music, the result was rock 'n' roll. It was no coincidence that the finest early exponents of rock came from the American South, where the rhythm 'n' blues influence was strongest. In the deep South racial discrimination was still prevalent in the mid-1950s, and much of the initial hostility to Elvis Presley arose from the feeling that he, a white Southern boy, was performing 'black' music.

While female teeny-boppers in this country screamed and swooned in the approved manner whenever Cliff Richard or Adam Faith appeared on and off stage, boys seem to have kept their strongest allegiance for the raunchy Americans. Opportunities to see as well as hear their idols were few and far between. Buddy Holly and the Crickets toured Britain in 1957, and Eddie Cochran was returning to

The Wild One (1954), starring brooding movie star Marlon Brando and immortalising American biker cults of the fifties, was banned by British film censors until 1968.

the USA following a successful British tour when he was killed in a car crash near London airport. Elvis Presley never performed in Britain, but at the end of his military service, on the evening of 2 March, 1960, he spent an hour on Scottish soil, changing planes at Prestwick airport *en route* to the USA from West Germany.

The 'youthquake' in the fifties assumed such alarming proportions that parents took fright. Hysterical girls, screaming their heads off at rock 'n' roll concerts, did little to allay their fears. Fan worship was nothing new — pop singers from Al Jolson to Frank Sinatra and movie

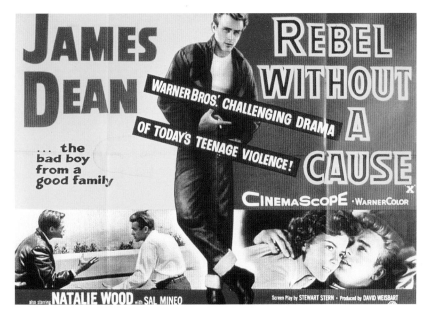

'Crazy mixed-up kids' in affluent Fifties' America were the theme of *Rebel Without a Cause*. The movie turned James Dean into a cult figure, the embodiment of the moody and rebellious teenager.

stars from Rudolph Valentino to Rock Hudson had received the homage of generations of delirious fans. But for the first time, TV brought such disturbing scenes of mass hysteria into the home. While working teenagers could now afford record players, many still lived with parents for whom rock 'n' roll music was anathema. The transistor radio was a consumer product with a special appeal for teenagers, and by the end of the decade it had become an integral part of the 'youth culture'.

When *Rock Around the Clock* was released in Britain in 1956, teenagers leapt from their seats and jived in the aisles. Frenzied youths wrecked rows of cinema seats. Twelve towns banned the movie, but Haley arrived in London in February 1957 to a rapturous re-

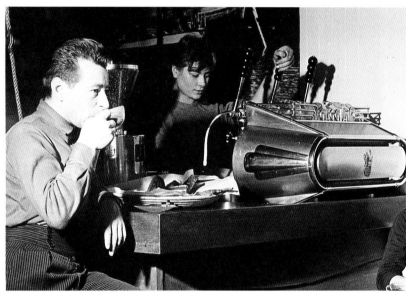

Coffee bars symbolised the new social mobility of the young. Tommy Steele, one of Britain's first American-style rock 'n' roll stars, initially performed in a London Espresso bar during breaks from serving refreshments.

ception from British fans. Movies such as *Rebel Without a Cause* and *The Wild One* emphasised the 'defiant' aspects of the new teenage sub-culture. Millions of youngsters worldwide copied the style and behaviour of James Dean, Marlon Brando and Elvis Presley.

In the USA, the teen scene increasingly revolved around drug stores and diners where soft drinks were consumed to the strident rhythm of the blaring juke-box. British teenagers patronised cafés and coffee bars where the favourite tipple was frothy espresso. The more stylish and cosmopolitan coffee bars were frequented by middle-class beatniks, whose loose black roll-neck sweaters and tapered pants were self-consciously 'arty'. Beatniks could quote from seminal novels of the period, such as Jack Kerouac's *On the Road* and J.D. Salinger's

The Catcher in the Rye, and were deliberately 'dressing down' to express their anti-Establishment viewpoint. Ironically, by the end of the decade the 'Beatnik Look' had been given a high-fashion profile by Yves Saint Laurent and other Parisian *couturiers*.

The Teddy boy fashion originated in Britain in the Coronation year

Good health advice from careful mothers: "Don't lend your comb, don't borrow others."

The affluent society of the late-fifties gave young people purchasing power and access to 'luxuries' such as Italian Vespa and Lambretta motor-scooters. Merchandisers and advertisers could no longer ignore teenage lifestyles.

of 1953. The style borrowed freely from the 'New Edwardian' fashion trend of wealthy young men-about-town and the costume of the Western gambler as mythologised by Hollywood. Teddy boys — known colloquially as 'teds' — were almost exclusively drawn from the urban working-class. They wore sideburns and were immensely

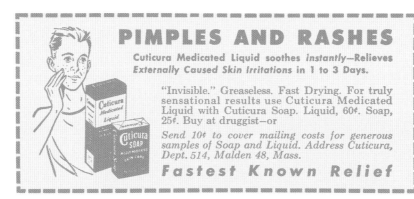

PIMPLES AND RASHES

Cuticura Medicated Liquid soothes *instantly*—Relieves
Externally Caused Skin Irritations in 1 to 3 Days.

"Invisible." Greaseless. Fast Drying. For truly
sensational results use Cuticura Medicated
Liquid with Cuticura Soap. Liquid, 60¢. Soap,
25¢. Buy at druggist—or

*Send 10¢ to cover mailing costs for generous
samples of Soap and Liquid. Address Cuticura,
Dept. 514, Malden 48, Mass.*

Fastest Known Relief

proud of their 'drapes' — broad-shouldered, knee-length jackets with velvet collars, modelled on the short 'Edwardian Look' overcoats made by exclusive Savile Row tailors. The jackets, in bright pink, deep purple, electric blue and other eye-catching colours, were worn with narrow 'drainpipe' trousers, string ties, and thick crêpe-soled suede

Zits were one of the few clouds on the horizon of fifties' teenagers, whose lifestyle now attracted the attention of advertisers and merchandisers.

shoes known as 'brothel creepers'. Teddy girls wore flouncy dirndl-style skirts with numerous paper nylon petticoats and flat shoes suitable for energetic jiving.

By the late-fifties skiffle, which originated in traditional jazz bands, reached the height of its short-lived popularity, and Scottish-born Lonnie Donegan was its self-proclaimed king. Apart from a guitar — available by mail order on 'easy terms' — all that were needed were an old-fashioned washboard for rhythm and a bass made out of a tea chest, broom handle and string. Over 500 skiffle groups sprang into existence in Britain alone, and far more skiffle music was played on *6.5 Special* than native rock 'n' roll. Thousands of teenagers hoped to emulate Donegan, who had earned at least £7000 from the sales of his 78 rpm record of 'Puttin' on the Style' and topped the bill at the London Palladium. Some were eventually successful beyond their wildest dreams — John Lennon and Paul McCartney first played together in a skiffle group called The Quarrymen, which they formed in 1956.

The teenagers of the fifties not only had jobs, incomes, tastes and opinions. The rise of rock 'n' roll promised members of their age group wealth and status previously reserved for magnates and movie stars. Tommy Steele, rocketing to stardom from humble employment as a £60 a month steward on the *Mauretania,* typified the 'rags to riches' transformation now possible, thanks to teenage purchasing power.

5

SOMETHIN' ELSE

Design for Living

Technology entered the home in a big way in the fifties and changed people's lives. *Avant-garde* designers experimented with new shapes and materials, but versatile and affordable 'contemporary' became the decade's most familiar design experience.

JUST WHAT IS IT THAT MAKES TODAY'S HOMES SO DIFFERENT, SO APPEALING? Richard Hamilton, 1956.

Seductive images of the new consumer society won recognition from *avant-garde* artists and critics, resulting in witty and innovative Pop Art, a milestone in the evaluation of popular culture.

Design for Living

WHICH OF THESE
HOOVER APPLIANCES
DOES MY WIFE WANT ?

In the 1950s millions of Americans and Europeans underwent a diaspora from congested inner cities to new towns and suburban estates. By 1958, one in every five people in Britain lived in new post-war homes. In some instances,

Lucky Me!

Bendix washing machines — like many other labour-saving devices — were marketed as invaluable aids to *womens'* work.

'Jet Age' styling helped sell the Pifco hairdryer, one of the new 'consumer durables'.

new built environments came complete with approved modern art in the form of pseudo-Henry Moore sculpture. In others they even lacked essentials such as schools, shops and roads. Uprooted and replanted millions were about to experience a new life, far from familiar landmarks and associations. An optimistic mood prevailed. Celebratory approaches to technology and science, characteristic of the fifties, were seen in the fully automated 'homes of the future' that were star attractions in housing exhibitions of the period. And didn't the gleaming domes of nuclear power plants such as the USA's

The fifties' ideal was a 'living kitchen' where the family sat down to informal meals. 'Dream kitchens' had matching, built-in appliances and easy-to-clean plastic work surfaces.

Argonne National Laboratory and Great Britain's Calder Hall signal 'Atoms for Peace' — a new era in atomic power 'for the benefit of mankind'?

From Brasilia to Berlin, modern architecture took shape in steel, glass, brick and concrete — especially the latter. Avant-garde architects Mies van der Rohe and Philip Johnson created sophisticated glass and steel boxes for adventurous clients. Even modest suburban development houses boasted picture windows. In new homes, rooms were frequently smaller than before and were

G-E Authorized Appliance Service is friendly, swift, nearby

unsuitable for bulky traditional furniture. A solution was at hand, however. Newspapers and magazines were already publicising mid-century modern, or 'contemporary' — an amalgam of design elements from Scandinavia, the USA and Italy, combining light-weight furniture with informal, 'open-planning'.

Until the fifties, only a small minority of people in Britain kept abreast of modern design ideas. The 1951 Festival of Britain, with the Council of Industrial Design responsible for the selection of 10,000 exhibits, came as a revelation to hundreds of thousands of Festival

where space really counts —

NEW **HOTPOINT** SUPER-18 with BIG·BIN

American living standards — reflected in this witty Hotpoint advertisement — set a precedent for other Western countries.

visitors for whom 'modern' had meant the art deco shapes and patterns of the inter-war era. The Design Centre in London opened in April 1956. By 1958 there were more than 8000 items in its reference library of 'approved' designs. In the Design Centre, young couples looking for furniture and furnishings could 'shop before buying', browsing at leisure before deciding on the solution best suited to their requirements. Unit furniture, like the highly popular G-Plan range in Britain, consisting of lightweight pieces that could be successfully combined to create a wide variety of room settings, was exhibited

Frigidaire's 1956 'Kitchen of Tomorrow' featured a planning desk with every convenience, from built-in vanity to television 'phone. A hot and cold drinks dispenser and an ultrasonic dishwasher were among the push-button 'labour-saving' gadgets on show.

'Contemporary' was a complete interior style, borrowing openly from Scandinavia, the USA and Italy, and combining light furniture with bright colours and lively patterns.

along with matching textiles and accessories.

TV sitcoms such as *I Love Lucy* and *The Life of Riley* raised American viewers' expectations regarding living standards. The shows, exported, had a similar effect abroad. 'Are you living in yesterday's house?' queried one American advertiser. 'Wouldn't you love a home insulated to stay warmer in winter, cooler in summer ... A scientifically planned kitchen with matching appliances, a waist-high, built-in oven ... a sound-treated ceiling that soaks up noise, helps you work in a more relaxed atmosphere? A home with extra bathrooms — generous closets — electric outlets galore — and a *real* dining room?'

Sophisticated, elegant and functional furniture designs by Charles Eames, George Nelson, Harry Bertoia and Eero Saarinen represented the upper, exclusive end of the market. And never before had even modest incomes commanded such a wide choice. In small houses and flats the main room, increasingly 'open-planned', served as lounge and dining room. The demarcation line was indicated by a librenza or

Room settings grew more informal under the impact of TV. Tables for plants, lamps and snacks were produced in new shapes, using fashionable materials such as stove-enamelled metal, ceramic tiles, lacquered brass, and plastics.

room divider, usually consisting of display units and shelves.

In the fifties, possession of a television set amounted to initiation into the new, 'buy now, pay later' consumer society, involving — as it did for many — a major credit transaction. TV was an important status symbol, maximum points being awarded to the owner of a console model with sliding doors and a 21-in. screen. The American-made Stromberg-Carlson 'Regency' came in a mahogany-veneered cabinet with a simulated marble top, gold-tooled leatherette door panels, and imported English porcelain door pulls. The 'Empire II' from the same manufacturer, described as 'a new concept in func-tional television design', had a cabinet of comb-grained limed oak or Honduras mahogany veneers, disappearing tambour doors, and 'exclusive 21-in. Panoramic Vision picture for extended room-wide viewing'. Expensive and 'technologically amazing' TV became the focal point of the living room, which now included low-slung 'TV armchairs' and a boomerang or palette-shaped coffee table. Tele-vision meals, prepared in advance and wheeled in on a trolly 'so that mother, too, can enjoy the evening programme uninterruptedly', became an established routine in many homes.

Lighting fixtures increasingly took the form of wall lights on flexible brackets, low-hanging clustered pendants, and two or three light free-standing lamps. Well-meaning attempts to produce lamps with slender curved lines resulted in shapes uncomfortably re-miniscent of the praying mantis. Houseplants enjoyed a vogue unprecedented since the turn of the century, and the fashionable contrasting wall treatments in many homes were enhanced by wall brackets containing trailing plants in colourful plastic pots. Pictorial wallpapers were frequently used to add distinction to a hall or dining area. Motifs such as architectural follies, Victorian fashions, hot air balloons, veteran cars and eccentric locomotives exploited veins of whimsy and nostalgia in a manner reminiscent of the celebrated Ealing comedy films of the period.

The 'ideal home', seen in glossy magazines, reflected the values of the upper classes and something of the minimalist philosophy of the avant-garde. But such high-minded abstinence had little or no appeal for ordinary Americans and Europeans, enjoying the benefits of a cheap consumer society for the first time. Many objects produced for the home and sold in tens of thousands were devoid of 'good design' as the pundits understood it. TV lamps with bases in the shape of Spanish dancers, Negro heads or ballerinas, and mirrors sprayed with glitter dust, were among the decorative accessories that enjoyed mass

Textile firms such as Liberty and Sanderson invited leading artists and designers to contribute to their 'contemporary' ranges.

Wire furniture by Harry Bertoia (1952). *Avant-garde* designers of the fifties skilfully used mid-century materials such as fibreglass, plywood, plastics and stainless steel wire.

Eero Saarinen's 1956 Pedestal range of chairs and tables, designed for Knoll International, could have come straight out of a fifties sci-fi movie.

appeal.

Plastic laminates and chipboard were used extensively for mass-produced furniture, now standing on splayed and tapered ebonised legs ending in brass ferrules. With the decade's commitment to new materials and the modern aesthetic, plastics entered the home in a big way: kitchenware, bathroom fittings, lampshades and curtains were just some of the plastic products soon taken for granted.

The kitchen was the most 'functional' room in the house, and the one, moreover, which contained the largest number of status symbols — electric appliances such as refrigerators, cookers, washers, food mixers and coffee percolators. In the USA the coveted built-in look

Interior of Philip Johnson's own 'Glass House', New Canaan, Connecticut. High Style houses encapsulated the new, relaxed mood of the fifties, with open plans and flowing space between living and dining areas.

of the customised 'dream kitchen' was achieved with the aid of Frigidaire 'Sheer Look' free-standing appliances, which 'slipped into place like Junior's building blocks' and came in such glamorous colours as Mayfair Pink, Stratford Yellow and Aztec Copper. The influence of American automobile stylists spread far beyond that industry. Soon refrigerators, washers and cookers were appearing with cosmetic chrome trim and rows of impressive-looking dials. Magazine ads showed immaculately dressed women presiding over kitchens full of gleaming 'labour-saving' gadgets. The inference was obvious if tenuous: with the necessary outlay on so-called consumer durables, 'women's work' could be virtually abolished.

The classic 'glass box' houses of Mies van der Rohe and Philip Johnson helped establish the vogue for picture windows in suburban houses.

50's Life and Style

6

SOMETHIN' ELSE

Time Out

ifties' América pioneered new leisure concepts. Time-Pay Plans enabled Americans to spread vacation costs over the year. Many took the opportunity to see for themselves a Europe known only through movies such as *An American in Paris.* Eventually, with greater travel opportunities, countless Europeans also experienced the sensation of being 'innocents abroad'.

SETTING OUT

For countless American families, unspoilt, spectacular
vacationlands lay at the end of a smooth automobile ride.
By the late-fifties a nationwide network of super-highways
was luring millions of new visitors each year to the USA's
National Parks, nature-endowed wonderlands containing
everything from a live volcano to dinosaur bones. Fifties'
Americans were able to discover the 'frontier spirit,' following the trail of Wild Bill Hickok and Calamity Jane, parti-
cipating in rodeos and Indian dances, and taking in such
astonishing sights as the giant Grand Coulee Dam.

Time Out

Motorists planning scenic routes across the USA enjoyed an unrivalled network of highways and services.

AMERICA'S NUMBER ① ROAD CAR!

Leisure and holiday horizons widened dramatically during the fifties. 'Labour-saving' appliances were eliminating much of the drudgery associated with household chores. TV and hi-fi were adding new dimensions to home entertainment, and rapidly increasing car ownership was bringing greater all-year-round mobility. Americans, already riding high on the great wave of post-war prosperity, were discovering their own vast country, motoring along the new interstate highways or relaxing in the observation lounges of express trains. The Great Northern Railway's *Western Star* stopped daily in Montana's Glacier National Park, where the passengers were greeted by 'real Blackfeet Indians' in full

ceremonial dress. Greyhound and Trailways carried city dwellers to such choice vacation spots as the Rockies, Yellowstone Park, the Grand Canyon and Niagara Falls. For a fare of 1348 dollars, Pan American Airways offered a round-the-world vacation trip — from the USA to the USA.

By 1950, American intercity buses were carrying nearly six times the entire population each year, at a cost which worked out at less than $1\frac{1}{2}$ cents per mile. Greyhound Lines, the world's largest intercity

Luxury travel, fifties' style. The liner *Queen Elizabeth* at her moorings in New York harbour.

bus system, and National Trailways operated rival fleets of express coaches in distinctive liveries of blue, red and silver. Greyhound's Scenicruisers had 'air-suspension ride', complete washroom facilities, and a raised observation deck. Greyhound Lines' *Amazing America* tours took in such spectacular sights as the Great Smoky Mountains and the Hoover Dam.

On American trains, glass-enclosed scenic domes provided breathtaking panoramic views of mountains, forests, lakes, canyons and deserts. The transcontinental services rivalled each other in the

provision of reclining coach seats, roomy public lounges, and de luxe dining facilities. Union Pacific's *City of Los Angeles* 'Domeliner' featured 'roof garden' dining in a domed dining car, and the Pullman lounge in the same train was panelled in colourful redwood. On the 'Vista-Dome' *North Coast Limited* — winner of the 1954 Passenger Service Award — your helpful stewardess was also a registered nurse.

Hawaii, a $4\frac{1}{2}$-day cruise from the USA by luxury liner, or $8\frac{1}{2}$ hours

The racing dog emblem of Greyhound Lines — by 1950 a nationwide American institution with a fleet of nearly 6000 blue-and-silver passenger coaches.

G
R
E
Y
H
O
U
N
D

by Stratocruiser, offered Americans an exotic travel experience with no passports or foreign exchange to worry about. American couples contemplating matrimony were urged to honeymoon in 'small, compact Britain', where prices, by US standards, were 'staggeringly low'. With a British Railways' 'Thrift Tour' ticket, up to 1000 miles of 'go-as-you-please' rail travel in Britain and Ireland cost only 30 dollars first class.

Many Americans came to Europe with preconceptions formed by Hollywood movies such as *An American in Paris*, *Brigadoon* and *Hans Christian Andersen*. Maybe as an antidote to the pressures of modern life in their booming country, American motorists were encouraged to 'ride the lonesome trail' in search of the legendary West of Wild Bill Hickok, Deadwood Dick, Jesse James, and other folk heroes and villains who had never had to worry about mortgage repayments.

Americans were becoming hooked on boats and, from inexpensive

Fifties' Americans enjoyed increased social mobility and benefited from a shift in economic emphasis, from work to leisure. Car ownership gave them freedom to explore their vast country.

Every Union Pacific Domeliner carried a staff of 35. For 200 miles, the *City of Portland* skirted the Columbia River Gorge, with magnificent views from the Astra Dome picture windows.

kit boat to ready-to-go cruiser, there was a range of options available to suit every budget. Outboard motors were produced with due attention to styling and, like American cars, had different sales images. Evintrude's 'Starflite II', with a nod in the direction of the *Zeitgeist*, had 'Jetstream drive' and put you 'in full command of the most commanding power afloat', while Johnson's 'Sea Horse' was 'gentle as a kitten — a *family* motor'.

For those who had time and money to spare, the great transatlantic liners still offered a unique travel experience. America's *United States*, Great Britain's *Queen Mary* and *Queen Elizabeth*, and the French Line's *Liberté, Ile de France* and *Flandre,* all made regular sailings from New York to Europe.

It was never easier to obtain a permanent record of that dream trip to Europe. The Kodak 'Medallion 8' movie camera weighed just 23 oz and was no bigger than the old-fashioned box cameras that many people still used for snapshot photography. 'Electric eye' movie cameras, 35mm cameras with push-button focusing, stereo cameras, Polaroid cameras: all promised superlative results — and in 'living

YOU'RE SAFE AND SURE
WHEN YOU TRAVEL BY
Pullman

THE VISTA-DOME *California Zephyr*

The most popular train between Chicago and Oakland - San Francisco
via Denver and Salt Lake City

WESTERN PACIFIC

Include Southern California via San Francisco without additional rail fare • PULLMANS • CHAIR CARS

colour'. What set stereo pictures apart was 'the magic of the third dimension'. Pictures taken with a stereo camera were 'so lifelike you feel you're still there'.

A vacation on a Western dude ranch, including meals and use of horses, could be had for as little as 60 dollars a week, or — just for a change — how about the Passion Play, with the Black Hills of South

Attentive service was a feature of American railroad dining cars, and every course was served with a big helping of scenery on the side.

"travelling by Domeliner
is one of the
happiest habits
I've ever acquired"

Ronald Reagan

The Canadian, in daily service between Montreal/Toronto and Vancouver, provided the world's longest scenic dome ride — 2,881 miles of ever-changing scenery. By daylight the Canadian Pacific streamliner travelled through Banff in the heart of the Canadian Rockies.

Dakota for a stunning backdrop? More adventurous travellers could join an American group to see the Soviet Union by coach at an all-inclusive cost of 495 dollars, from Helsinki or Warsaw. Retired people could follow the sun all the year round in a 'New Moon' mobile apartment home, as featured in the MGM movie *The Long, Long Trailer*, starring Lucille Ball and Desi Arnaz. Designed 'for semi-permanent living, travel and vacation fun', the 'New Moon' came completely furnished and ready to live in.

In that pre-jumbo jet era, transcontinental flight still had plenty of style. The Lockheed Super Constellation was described as 'the largest, roomiest airliner in the world', with a de luxe Starlight Lounge designed by Henry Dreyfuss. In 1957 TWA introduced a luxurious Lockheed Starliner service called the 'Jetstream' and enthused that the giant four-engined airliners could fly at high altitudes, over bad weather, and could even take advantage of the smooth winds of the upper air. The aircraft were capable of flying from Los Angeles to Paris non-stop with fuel to spare and, as an added bonus, each plane featured an original mural.

The British Overseas Airways Corporation revolutionised air travel with pure jet de Havilland Comets as early as 1953, but America's first commercial jetliners — the Boeing 707 and the Douglas DC-8 — did

not enter service until the end of the decade. On the eve of the exciting new age of commercial jet flight, Donald W. Douglas, President and Chairman of the Douglas Aircraft Company, extolled the advantages of a shrinking world in which travellers would be able to lunch in Paris and dine in Manhattan. The Douglas DC-8 jetliner would fly eight miles above the earth . . . 'in the stratosphere', where 'occasionally the sun's rays filter through a crystal mist and sparkle like gems tossed on velvet'.

Mass tourism really began in the fifties. With some three million Britons travelling abroad every year, the package tour had evidently arrived to stay, and travel agents' windows were decked with colourful sun, sea 'n' sand posters which brought a whiff of the Côte d'Azur to every High Street in the country. Until the mid-fifties, British companies offering cheap package holidays abroad chartered trains instead of planes, and London's Victoria and Waterloo stations were thronged with holiday crowds waiting for their travel couriers before boarding trains for the Continent. Interestingly, in view of the long journeys undertaken on American railroads, British tour organisers limited their operations to places that were within twenty-four hours' travel by rail, since they felt that their customers

Leisure had never before held out so many tantalising — and affordable — possibilities. Holidays abroad were no longer the prerogative of the rich.

With TWA's Time Pay
Plan you paid 10% down,
flew to the sun, and paid
the balance over a year
or more in equal monthly
instalments.

Breakfast in bed was a
feature of Pan American
Airways' first-class
round-the-world
President service.

would not care to spend two nights on a train.

Thomas Cook & Son, a British institution founded in 1841, virtually invented the package tour in the nineteenth century, and in the fifties they successfully adapted to changing social conditions, offering a 15-day holiday in France for only £6 17s 6d. But Cook's old-established image was not necessarily an asset in the iconoclastic late-fifties, and the ever-growing legions of first-time travellers abroad appear to have had just as much confidence in new names such as Cosmos and Horizon.

One of the problems facing package tour operators of the fifties was the lack of suitable accommodation, which mainly consisted of *pensions* and superannuated Grand Hotels straight out of novels by Ouida and Vicki Baum. By the late-fifties, purpose-built resorts such as the Costa del Sol and Costa Blanca were emerging, well supplied with hotels specially designed for the new mass tourist market. Unlike the stately ornamental piles of the *fin-de-siècle*, they were built of reinforced concrete, breeze blocks and bricks, rendered in dazzling white stucco. In America, Morris Lapidus established a precedent for the movie-set hotels of the new era of mass tourism. Hotels such as the Eden Roc, Americana and Fontainebleau were

Parked cars at San Francisco's famous Fisherman's Wharf.

THE LURLINE IS HAWAII

Bermuda, Hawaii and the Bahamas were
tops with sun-seeking Americans.

Holidaymakers of the fifties recorded their travels with easy-to-use movie cameras.

tongue-in-cheek creations providing 'a sense of heightened excitement' appropriate to an annual two-week vacation. They were perfect hotels for the admass age, hotels *à la* Hollywood. And the lesson was not lost on architects working on the other side of the Atlantic. Gradually European hotels ceased to be 'superior' relics of a bygone era and instead reflected the essentially classless ethos of the consumer society.

Most Britons, of course, still took their holidays in their own country, touring by coach or making the best of the British summer at seaside resorts such as Morecambe and Bournemouth. In the early years of the decade they flocked to Billy Butlin's holiday camps, where thousands of ex-servicemen and women experienced *déjà vu* at the nostalgic sight of serried rows of wooden huts.

Though millions were by now addicted to television, 'live' entertainment still commanded huge and enthusiastic support. For jazz lovers, the fifties was a legendary decade of dazzling virtuosity, with performers of the calibre of Charlie Parker, Miles Davis, Gerry Mulligan and John Coltrane. From traditional Dixieland, through West Coast 'cool' to mainly black, East Coast 'hard bop', jazz was played and promoted at concerts and festivals and heard on radio, films, TV and records. The Newport, Rhode Island, Jazz Festival was founded in 1954 by George Wein, and the 1959 Festival, featuring more than fifty of America's top jazz musicians, was immortalised in the 1960 Technicolor movie *Jazz on a Summer's Day*. 'Cool' and 'square' were terms borrowed from the world of jazz which achieved

Movies such as *Moulin Rouge* and hit songs like 'Under The Bridges of Paris' sent large numbers of Americans in search of the magic of 'Gay Paree'.

wide currency by the end of the decade.

On a tight budget, time out could simply mean a night at the movies, which were more exciting than ever before, thanks to such revolutionary inventions as Cinemascope, Vistavision, Cinerama, Todd AO and 3-D. The latter was a short-lived fashion, but while it lasted millions shuddered pleasurably as all sorts of objects came hurtling at them from out of the wide screen.

In the fifties Hollywood's prestige was still untarnished. World-wide, countless millions looked to Tinseltown for dream fulfilment and were seldom disappointed. Television had tremendous novelty value, but there were no TV programme equivalents of Hollywood's big-budget movies. Musicals such as *Seven Brides for Seven Brothers*, Westerns such as *Shane*, epics such as *The Robe* and *The Ten Commandments*, were seen on *big* screens, and there was no shortage of crowd-pulling names. John Wayne, Marilyn Monroe, Tony Curtis, Marlon Brando, Kirk Douglas and Doris Day were just a few of the

Immortal jazzmen: Charlie 'Bird' Parker and Miles Davis. Parker, who died in 1955, played his last gig in March of that year at Birdland, a club named in his honour.

stars who glittered in the Hollywood firmament. Westerns have always been popular, and the Hollywood of the 1950s produced Westerns of the calibre of *High Noon, Gunfight at the OK Corral*, and *Rio Bravo*. American 'corporation men' coping with the complexities of life in mid-century USA may have envied the lifestyles of resourceful riverboat gamblers and hard-riding gunslingers. The sci-fi movie trend was understandable in view of the decade's infatuation with science and technology. But many of the movies also reflected the paranoid mood of 'McCarthy era' USA, and aliens landing in the America of the early 1950s met with a less friendly reception than 'E.T.' a generation later.

The United States in the fifties witnessed a tremendous boom in open-air movies. Like supermarkets and shopping centres, the 'ozones', as they were sometimes called, were a phenomenon of the automobile age and the decentralised society. The world's first open-air drive-in movie theatre was opened in 1933, at Camden, New Jersey. Early drive-ins were fairly primitive and owners of plush movie houses contemptuously dismissed them as 'passion pits', but by the early-fifties, just as many orthodox picture theatres were closing, open-air drive-ins were entering their golden age. By 1956 there were more than 5000 drive-in movie theatres in the USA and

Canada, and the largest theatres had space for 1000 or more cars. Texas alone had 472 drive-ins, some of which provided rails where riders could tether their horses while watching the movies from their saddles.

Apart from the movie screen, which had to be sturdy enough to withstand high winds, the fundamentals of the drive-in were parking space, ramps which elevated the car windshields towards the screen, and in-car speakers. To these essentials, enterprising operators added refreshment stands and gimmicks such as nurseries, playgrounds and open-air dance floors. Several Texas drive-ins provided a laundry service: patrons left their washing at the entrance and collected it, freshly laundered, as they left. Some drive-ins offered in-car electric heaters for cold nights. In Chicago's giant Double Drive-In, two movies were shown simultaneously on opposite sides of the huge metal screen. The plushier drive-ins were landscaped, with neon entrances, and were seen to advantage on warm summer evenings, when the stars above and on the Technicolor screen combined to produce an effect of eerie glamour.

In fifties' America the 'Drive-In' flourished while attendances slumped at orthodox movie theatres.

Montgomery Clift — acclaimed as a major movie star after his performance in *From Here to Eternity* (1953) — became America's number one teen idol of the early-fifties, precursor of anti-hero James Dean.

At the height of the 3-D movie craze, Britain's *Picture Post* featured glamour girl Sabrina's sensational cleavage in three-dimensional colour!

PICTURE
POST

FIRST EVER
COLOUR 3-D
IN THIS ISSUE
Sabrina's new role

COLOUR 3-D: FREE SPECTACLES WITH THIS ISSUE
BEST WAR NOVEL YET: 'H.M.S. ULYSSES' BEGINS TODAY
BIGGEST WEEKLY CASH COMPETITION: £1,500 IN PRIZES

The naïveté of the fifties, the first mass-consumerist decade, can never be recaptured. Cars no longer sport tail-fins, and TVs don't come complete with door pulls of genuine English porcelain. Teenagers have lost the power to shock merely by dressing differently from their elders.

Since the fifties, the consumer society has spread across the world. More people now have more of everything than ever before. Miniature 'personal' TVs and stereos are commonplace. Modern advertising and image-building techniques are altogether more subtle and sophisticated than those described by Vance Packard over thirty years ago. Although the majority of people in the developed countries are more prosperous than ever before, millions worldwide now question the very idea of unlimited economic growth, with its implied exploitation of Third World countries and waste of natural resources.

The fifties was indeed a decade of comparative innocence, when the 'obedient atom', suitably stylised, adorned curtains, clocks and TV ornaments. A decade when interplanetary liners seemed no more far-fetched than any of the other daily 'miracles of science', and many people believed that when life on earth became un-tenable, then we would simply don our spacesuits, blast off *en masse*, head into the empyrean, and carry civilisation — complete with consumer credit, TV commercials and Coca-Cola — to other, virgin worlds.

- W·S·GRANDISON -

CREDITS

ARCHITECTURAL ASSOCIATION
102, 103a, 103b

BBC HULTON PICTURE LIBRARY
35a, 36, 53, 62, 78, 82, 85a, 99, 118, 122, 124-125

BLACK STAR
40-41

BPCC/ALDUS ARCHIVE
101a

RICHARD BRYANT
52a

MAX ERNST
93

JOHN FRENCH COLLECTION
46, 47a, 47b

O.D. GALLAGHER LTD
12a

WILLIAM GRANDISON
9, 11, 12b, 13a, 13b, 15, 31, 34, 37, 39, 44-45, 56b, 63,
65, 73, 79, 86a, 91, 95, 123, 126, 127

HARRY HAMMOND
81

ROBERT HUNT LIBRARY
43b, 98b, 115

THE KEYSTONE COLLECTION
20, 51, 74, 84, 86b

MACDONALD/ALDUS ARCHIVE
101b

TONY MORRISON
52b, 52c

NATIONAL FILM ARCHIVE
16-17, 87a

JIM NICHOL
77a, 80

OBELIST BOOKS
50a

POPPERFOTO
14b, 22, 27, 50b, 50c, 85b, 88, 98a, 105, 119

DAVID REDFERN PHOTOGRAPHY
83, 121

SYNDICATION INTERNATIONAL LTD
43c